Visions
of
Johanna

Peter Sarno

Johanna, an artist, and Matt, a music critic, couldn't be more different, but by a simple twist of fate, she plucks him from a crowd at a Dylan concert. What follows is a heady and intense relationship buffeted by the usual suspects that gently rocked the '80s. Matt's lessons in art—as well as life—at the hands of Johanna, drive the novel into pockets of feminism and quiet revolution. All of this is tempered by deeply held traumatic secrets that torque their intimacy.

Yet it's Revere—and not Boston—that remains one of the underlying attractions in *Visions of Johanna*. This north shore backdrop brings Matt into full focus—a child in a city of recent immigrants, life by the ocean, the bilious flavor of the Mob are just some of the elements rendered in skillful detail.

A meditation on art and unrest, *Visions of Johanna* celebrates life, love, memory and the undying power of the deep connections that sustain us. The novel follows Johanna and Matt as they pursue their dreams to paint and to write. But burdening problems collide with these artistic desires and other forces conspire against them. Ultimately, the two are done in by their inability to share aspects of their past they believe they must hide from.

The novel travels through time and social unrest to the final moment hinted at in the prologue. Within this book's pages, tragedies haunt, acts of moral goodness manifest themselves, and benevolence reigns with a finality that absolves all.

PUBLISHERS' CATALOGING-IN-PUBLICATION DATA
Names: Sarno, Peter, author.
Title: Visions of Johanna / Peter Sarno.
Description: Byfield, MA : PFP Publishing, [2023]
Identifiers: ISBN: 979-8-9866266-0-4 (paperback)
Subjects: LCSH: Women artists--Northeastern States--Fiction. |
Music critics--Northeastern States-- Fiction. | Man-woman rela-
tionships--Fiction. | Social conflict--United States--History--20th
century--Fiction. | Feminism--United States--History--20th cen-
tury--Fiction. | Nineteen eighties--Fiction. | Secrecy--Fiction. |
LCGFT: Historical fiction.
Classification: LCC: PS3619.A747 V57 2023 | DDC: 813/.6--dc23

For Nanette Louise
&
In loving memory of
Mary Ann Tranfaglia
(1955 – 1971)

Acknowledgments

First, to my wife, Nanette, thank you. A steadfast reading advocate starting with your son and the *Frog and Toad* series, to the years spent nurturing your granddaughter via the ongoing adventures of *Amelia Bedelia, Pinkalicious,* and *Ariel.* You still read several novels a week—proving that fiction matters and the trust ceded to authors should not be taken for granted. I'll always be grateful for your support and love, but do hope this book is able to pass your "first fifty pages" test.

For nearly three years, Martha Carlson Bradley, performed developmental editing services for this novel with loving care and expertise. The book would not exist without your unending guidance and encouragement. I remain indebted to your professionalism and friendship.

To Catherine Parnell, thank you for your line editing and publicist duties and for "getting" it. Your belief in the merits and value of the story and its characters has given me the confidence to sustain my journey as a writer.

Susan DeNoble Doherty, you are an artist of tremendous courage. Thank you for allowing me to use your drawing on the front cover. But more importantly, for your tenacity in holding firm to your visions—no matter the consequences—for your lessons in love and life, and for your faith in me several decades ago when I barely believed in myself.

To Roland Merullo, my brother from another mother, you're always just a phone call away, and that's not simply some trite phrase. You've been there for me day and night, through good times and bad; your loyalty and friendship heartens and buoys me.

To Ioanna Opidee, I'm extremely grateful for your read of an early version of the manuscript as well as your insightful commentary and suggestions.

Brother Joe Torra—a friend since I was your teaching assistant in grad school—you continue to provide an honorable example by living the unflinching life of an artist and always remaining supportive to those of us who dare to struggle in the arts. I admire and appreciate you.

To Joe Dimino, who first taught me that Greenland is colder than Iceland :) Beyond the factual elements of that lesson, you reminded me to not make decisions based on surface level appearances or first impressions. A mentor and friend, you did not hesitate to read my very early and feeble efforts at short stories and novels decades ago and somehow seemed to find value in the work—and me. Thanks for listening and your many acts of kindness.

Cheryl Nixon, you're an extraordinary professor and person. You fought with a passion to get me my first teaching gig at UMass Boston. Thank you.

Askold Melnyczuk, I'm grateful for your reverence of the written word and for introducing me to the works of Susan Cheever, Ann Patchett, Roland Merullo, and many others in your graduate memoir course.

Beth Harrington, singer, filmmaker, and trailblazer, thank you for being such wonderful company during the 80s, for letting me drag you to numerous plays and other events, for acting in one of my directing class projects at the Loeb (remember that?) and, for dragging *me* to a Prince concert during his Purple Rain tour which I had absolutely no interest in attending at the time but now realize was a historic event.

My thanks also to Ellie Marshall for our endless and enthusiastic discussions of music — a conversation that began over forty years ago; to Steve Forbert for your musicianship, fortitude, example, and friendship; to Dawn Faria, chemo nurse extraordinaire, and the radiation team, as well as other members of my care group at Dana Farber — including Doctors Margalit, Sehgal, and Sethi.

Dr. Sherry Soleymani, thank you for your unwavering compassion and diligence. Dr. Mike Morley, I'm grateful for your patience and knowledge.

Mike Pinto at Country Press, thanks for going beyond the call of duty these last several years. Carol Sacco, your unfailing smile, optimism, and sense of humor while manning the desk at the Byfield Post Office always make my days brighter.

Thank you to Linda, Laura, Paul, and my late Mom and Dad. To Alexandra, Juliana, and Amanda — Three-of-a-Kind who will beat a Royal Flush any day of the week. To Dale at Porter Square Books; Mary and Jaime at Newtonville Books; Dan at the Water Street Bookstore, Roxie at the Broadside Bookshop, Michael at Gibson's Bookstore, Stan and Chris at Northshire Bookstore, Steve and Dawn at Stillwater Books, Jennifer and my Pathway Book Service family, and to the many other supportive Indie bookstore owners.

Thanks to Nick Buonopane, I think of you as a son—despite our many differences. To Debbie Wentworth-Penta, one of the sweetest and kindest people I knew while growing up. To John Dimino and Judy Rapoza, and to the brave girls and women I've met in my life as well as the ones I hope to meet in the future.

To my granddaughter Faith Joy who remains—without a doubt—the greatest gift I have ever been lucky enough to greet. I never dreamed you might be fighting some of these same battles for freedom and equality some four decades later, I wish members of your generation success and the courage to continue.

And finally, to you the reader, thank you for taking a chance on this story.

East Boston — 2012

Johanna named her only child Faith, just about the time she started to lose hers and the life she'd always dreamt of had begun to slip away. Now, some twenty-five years later, it's Faith's voice on the line, telling me the news.

I hang up the phone and put pen to paper, convinced my letter's sole purpose is to provide Faith with some history by illustrating how her mother had once been an uncompromising force. There might be another reason as well. I guess I need to prove to myself I'd been a part of Johanna's world and it somehow still matters.

After several stops and starts, and three abysmal drafts—all of which I toss in the trash—I call Faith back to accept her invitation for a visit and then make plans to rent a car and head to upstate New York.

Johanna

— 1 —

With Chelsea rents on the rise and 1980s condo mania in full bloom, I faced another eviction process—my second in the three years that had passed since college graduation. If the work of leaving still one more apartment hadn't been stressful enough, the fact I'd be moving in with my sixty-four-year-old mother for several months until I found a new place had set me on edge.

Two Landmark hardcover books—jutting out in protest from the top of an improperly secured packing carton—forced me to grapple with its four flaps again. I bungled the folding sequence, tore the cover open, then locked the box before sliding it next to one with the words "old bills" scribbled in sharpie above a crossed out "office supplies."

Countless others covered the floor. Marred by scars, they sported remnants of shiny tape that dangled like days-old Band-Aids on skinned knees. Feeling overwhelmed by the clutter surrounding me, I stepped outside to buy lunch at a deli.

"Ah, it's you."

Mr. Pressman jammed a slab of meat on the slicer's tray, moved it back and forth a few times, and handed me a thin cut. "Tell me. Where you-gonna-go to beat a piece of brisket like that?"

He chomped on an unlit cigar, placed the fingers of his right hand on his thumb, and gestured in my direction. Then he unscrewed the lid from a jar and pushed pickles towards me—their aroma pungent yet oddly comforting.

I grabbed one and thanked him—fingers dripping.

"Italians. . . . *cosa sai della vita?*" he said.

"You're right."

Though good-natured ribbing, he would never let me live down the day he caught me walking out of Dimino's—the store across the street—sub sandwich bag evident in hand.

I picked up a few packages of chips and gave my order of corned beef on rye to the cashier. Pressman sent me another uncomplimentary signal before turning to face a different customer.

On the way back to my place, I ran into Alejandra Lopez, and distributed the chips to her three fatherless—but freshly scrubbed and neatly dressed—kids in tow. Rachel tried to open hers, and Alejandra tapped her lightly on the arm. "What did I tell you? Say, 'thank you, *sir*'!"

The four-year-old girl looked up timidly. "Thanks, Matt." The other two children echoed her before digging into their bags.

Though Alejandra's blouse was perpetually wrinkled and untucked, and her jeans were often sullied by obscure stains, her hair—pitch-black and lustrous—flowed elegantly atop her right shoulder in a single tightly woven braid. The Dahlia, or other vibrant flower typically pinned to it, could never match the intensity of her eyes. She smiled, mouthed her gratitude, and crossed the road to avoid our neighbor's thriving drug business—replete with a convenient drive-through first-floor window his customers were compelled to ride up on curb and sidewalk to reach.

This scene from *No Exit* had been reenacted at least twice per week. Sometimes I'd replace the chips with Hoodsie cups, sandwiches, or bagels. It was as if their mother strove to light the wick of a candle inside a dark and drafty cave, and no matter how frequently that flame went out, Alejandra braced herself to strike another match.

At that phase of my life—at any, I guess—there

was something to be said for having a sense of identity and home. Strange as it may sound, there were times I'd feel grounded by inspecting litter on the streets: those popsicle sticks flung by Mrs. Kinsella that piled up while she struggled to quit smoking, the self-prescribed two-per-evening Seagram's VO nips of Florence Johnson, Tom Feinstein's Camel butts, and the phantom Goya sliced-carrot labels that drifted by whenever a slight breeze blew in.

Aware I had no right to bitch, I was concerned about the effect this influx of young professionals would have on the other tenants in my building—especially Mrs. Busby, who grew up with my late grandfather. She'd call—almost daily—for help to reset the clock on her microwave, but she really hoped I'd read letters from her grandchildren because her eyesight had been failing. Homemade and mostly charred chocolate chip cookies were usually served during those visits.

Later, I'd wonder if I'd garnered and spun this cast of characters as strands in a cocoon to insulate me—believing their pain was worse than my own.

Boxes and plastic bins—full of books, records, clothes, tapes, and CDs—cluttered my rooms. I filtered through stuff I'd lugged to three separate apartments; but my pace had been slow. On one pile lay a card for my sixteenth birthday given to me by my Aunt Marcia and Uncle Tony and a small, blue, felt-covered book commemorating my senior prom titled "Here Comes the Sun" complete with that night's menu which listed "Rainbow Fudge Fantasy" as dessert. I didn't remember that dish—although it sounded delicious—or much else from the event.

Other items were a postcard to my parents from The Boy's Club overnight camp, letting them know the experience was *just like the Army. We wake up at 6:45 with lights out at 9:00. We have taps at night. And if there is an important notice, Rojar (the Director) blows his whistle 3 times . . . ;* a memorial program from my dad's funeral held at Saint Anthony's Church; a snapshot of me at Fort George Citadel in Halifax, Nova Scotia—and another on the steps of the Cathedral in Washington; the playbill from *Speaking Out of Character*, a work written by Susan Weinberg—a creative writing classmate—and sponsored by the National Organization for Women, which starred Estelle Parsons and contained lyrics to "Bread and Roses."

I also found a Polaroid photo of my neighborhood friends Heather and Scott sitting in a dory, the name Holt's Pier on its side. After rubbing dust off that picture, I looked at their smiles and the boat's chipped paint, then placed it gently into a spiral-

5

bound notebook lying on my bed.

I discovered a green (BP) Dinosaur refrigerator magnet; my kindergarten report card from the Sunshine School in Winthrop, which included such categories as "I like to try new things," "I can tell stories," and "I share," as well as a handwritten note from the teacher that said *"Matthew is capable of better coloring than he is doing"*; and finally, a Topps baseball card that featured every player and coach from the 1967 Boston team, on which Heather had taken a black pen and scrawled the phrase "Red Sox Suck!" across the top.

Had I kept this shit because I'd convinced myself someone might be interested in it one day? Or were they collected as landmarks of a history I could hardly recall living?

My goldfish stared at me from his half-full bowl on the bureau and wiggled while waiting for an answer.

I walked downstairs and knocked on Mrs. B's door. Maybe the cookies wouldn't be burned to a crisp this time. Either way, I needed to hear words from family—even if the letter she asked me to read hadn't come from mine.

— 2 —

Several days later—living mostly out of boxes by then—I stood outside Hartford's Bushnell Memorial Hall. A woman about five foot two walked in front of me and struggled to keep a large painting more than half her size from falling onto the ground. With one hand, she smoothed the edges of wrapping paper torn at a corner of the frame, while her other hung on precariously. I offered to help by lifting an end and finding our way through a gathering crowd. I was covering a Bob Dylan concert as a music critic for the *Real Paper*—the neglected stepchild of Boston's more legitimately regarded weekly, the *Phoenix*.

The doors hadn't opened to ticket holders, but the woman caught the attention of a security guard and pleaded with him to pass the work on to Dylan. Free of her burden, she edged into the throng. A few people nearby stopped talking and looked at her. She wore a long coat that might more aptly be described as a patchwork quilt wrap—consisting of various pieces of colored fabric woven together into a background of navy blue. Many of these patches featured symbols: candles, starbursts, and unicorns. She also sported a dark derby encircled by a ribbon of pink lace. Softly spun and light blonde curls escaped from beneath it. I struck up a conversation; her name was Johanna.

More and more scalpers mingled and hawked tickets for the show. Five dollars for fifteen dollar seats and creeping lower.

"Two for tonight," one guy shouted.

"I've got four," yelled another.

Until that point, Dylan's "Gospel" tour had been panned. Long-term fans didn't know what to make of songs like "When You Gonna Wake Up," "Saving Grace," and "Gotta Serve Somebody," along with others of that ilk he'd thrown into the mix—not to mention Bob's newfound propensity to intersperse sermons throughout the shows.

A few nights before, in Worcester, Massachusetts, he'd advised us "following Jesus was no easy trip, but the *only* trip . . ." Then, apparently missing the irony, he warned, *"Cursed is the man who trusts in man,"* —as well as other varied quotes from the Bible.

These absolutes—espoused by the same artist who once celebrated life's ambiguities in tunes like "Blowing in the Wind" and "Only a Pawn in Their Game"—horrified most of his followers.

In a surprising twist, it was reminiscent of Dylan's so-called "Judas" phase of the mid '60s—when fans would storm out as soon this previously pure-folkie replaced his acoustic guitar with an electric model during the second half of a show. A recent newspaper headline dubbed the current tour "God-Awful Gospel" while another cautioned its readers "Born Again Dylan Leaves Audiences Behind" and one mocked, "Praise the Lord, Dylan Saved!"

In the end, these responses didn't paint an entire picture. Several present—including Johanna and me—intended to keep an open mind.

"Aren't you afraid he'll never see it?" I asked Johanna—referencing her artwork.

"Won't matter if he does or not. It's just my way of saying 'thank you.' For giving us inspiration and hope."

With that comment, Johanna appeared gracious and generous, while, in contrast, I had become the type of person who tried to figure out the other guy's angle. Would these differences pose a problem? Strange, I found myself already thinking about a future for us and I hadn't even learned her last name.

"Killer hat," someone said to Johanna.

I turned around. Luminous green eyes struck me; glitter sparkled in her hair.

Members of Hartford's Faith Assembly of God milled through the waiting crowd, passing out two-by-two-inch red-covered copies of *The Personal Bible: Verses of Comfort, Assurance, and Salvation.* An impeccably dressed young man wearing a boutonniere with a trio of white carnations handed one to each of us, introducing himself as Michael. I opened it and discovered a place to write your name and address on the title page—although for this impossibly slight-sized tome, with its tiny pages, I guessed first initials and post office box numbers would have to suffice. It reminded me of a prayer book I received from my grandparents at First Communion.

Prying into people's private beliefs and religions had never been my thing; still I asked Michael how he'd been introduced to the church.

He smiled and told his story.

I expected Johanna to roll her eyes and use that moment as an excuse to walk away and never see me again; to my surprise, she was keen to hear his answer as well.

Michael had moved from one foster placement to

the next, got adopted late—at ten—and then was welcomed into a home where children from diverse backgrounds had been cared for. For the first time, he had a genuine family with the people of his congregation being extended members.

"I hope to pass on that sense of belonging," he said.

A thin scar stretched from near the bottom of Michael's left ear down to a split on his top lip; I wondered if that wound might also have something to do with his membership, but didn't ask.

Unlike the *Watchtower* and *Awake* magazines I guiltily discarded in the moments following a Jehovah's Witness visit as soon as they'd turn from my door, I would hold on to this bit of "good news" for a while longer.

When concert-goers shuffled in, Johanna hugged me. She slipped a light purple business card into my hand; her name was framed by a unicorn-like cloud, a quarter moon, and two stars. "Meet outside after?" she said, more statement than question.

I'd scored a press pass and orchestra seats.

While Johanna's tickets were mezzanine.

Though the audience would have its share of no-shows, and a slim chance of a sellout existed, I didn't know how it would ever be possible for the two of us—just a couple of random concert-goers a half hour before—to find each other again among the thousands of other post-gig attendees. Besides, a part of Johanna struck me as Mystic-lite because of the manner she'd been dressed, her glitter, and that too-good-to-be-true earnestness. She also had to be several years older than me while I was "a thousand miles behind," as Dylan might've sung.

Oh, ye of little faith, my miniature red Bible would've chided me—if I'd even be able to locate that passage in the two-inch abridged version still in my hand.

Far from disappointed, I enjoyed the performance. "Pressing On" and "Ain't Gonna Go To Hell for Anybody" stood out—owing to the tightness of Dylan and his accompanying band, as well as the optimistic drive in his lyrics. I could've done without his evangelical—almost fire and brimstone—raps between tunes, but the show had been an unexpectedly pleasant experience.

I solicited comments for my *Real Paper* article and received a mixed bag of replies in return. Some audience members were transfixed and energized, while others called Dylan a "sellout."

Despite my better instincts, I hesitated, ran my

fingers along a few merchandise tables, stopped to skim the pages of a magazine or two, and poked through an assortment of commemorative t-shirts strung on hangers. Before I left the building, I peered the length of its long hallways a few times. Once outside, I inhaled deeply and welcomed the weed-free, fresh night air. Just about to head for my car, I felt a tug on my jacket. Another hug greeted me when I turned around.

"I love him! He's so damn good!" Johanna said.

She locked her arm in mine and we walked towards the parking lot.

How could I not take this opportunity to suggest we go for coffee—or something stronger?

While trying to figure out what joint in the area might still be open and summon the courage to ask her, a man marched straight in our direction. Stepping aside, I gave him clearance to pass, but he leaned in and kissed Johanna.

"Matthew, this is Ted. A Dylan fan. *Not!*"

Somewhat sheepishly and hoping to draw as little attention as possible, I extricated my arm from Johanna's and offered a snatch of obligatory small talk.

"You missed a great show," I said.

"Yeah?"

"The band found a tight groove . . ."

After I spat those words out, I realized how positively lame they sounded—and *I* was supposed to be the music critic.

"Not quite 'Like A Rolling Stone' I guess," Ted said.

"No."

I lifted my right foot, inspecting the soles of my sneaker for a tack or piece of gum I knew wasn't embedded there, and pondered telling Ted how the fervent intensity of "Pressing On" moved me and the couple sitting two rows over—so much so we rose from our seats and danced and clapped in rhythm to the song. Or, how the entire hall—so invigorated by the crescendo-building energy of "Ain't Gonna Go To Hell"—cheered so loud and long the band had to stop playing the next tune—one they had already started three times—until the noise died down.

But Ted wasn't a Dylan fan. And when I looked at a beaming Johanna—who appeared to be eager for a male bonding ritual to take place—I was certain I didn't want to share my feelings with him and had no interest in what dwelled on *his* mind.

"Creative use of stage lighting," I said.

"Yeah?"

"Yeah."

I studied the ground again before Johanna piped in and encouraged me to call her sometime and visit her art studio—"Not far from here. In Avon . . ."

She hugged me a third time. I fumbled in my pocket for keys before awkwardly shaking Ted's hand—the key chain still in mine—and headed for the lot.

Before tossing Johanna's business card into the glove compartment, I flipped it over and read *definition: artist / disciple, abundant, restless, /capable, practicing, skillful. / maintains visual dialogue, /meets life with a magic mind.*

I drove north towards Route 84, the Pike, and Boston.

On autopilot, and surprised I had reached the Mass state line so soon, I slowed down to pay the toll, reflecting on Dylan and the songs he played that night. What impelled a person to change direction so drastically?

I glanced in my rearview mirror and thought I saw Michael's carnations; but they were only white highway strips marking lanes.

15

— 3 —

I ended up covering other venues during the East Coast leg of Dylan's tour. These places included Portland, Maine, and Providence, Rhode Island. The setlist and script unfolded in much the same fashion: musicians still in sync—perhaps even more so—boos, worse than those in Connecticut, and a defiant artist who gave no quarter. Many outraged audience members must have felt destined to play the part of persecutors in the continuing mythical saga that had become the Dylan legacy.

And the singer obliged. Although, occasionally, he offered a plea for patience and understanding that went something like "Ah. Come on now."

Rather than be flustered by these confrontations, the five-foot-seven-inch Dylan—dwarfed by his lead guitarist, bass player, keyboardist, drummer and four backup singers—often indulged in perverse attempts to spur his detractors on.

After I'd put the *Real Paper* article to bed, tallied my expenses—several rolls of 35 millimeter film, fuel, meals—I discovered I might've earned a whopping $55. Though worth it to see my byline in print, I'd gotten paid more for Dylan's accompanying picture than for the piece itself.

During the previous few months, I'd questioned my job as a reviewer. Some critics and essayists I admired—Russell Baker, Studs Terkel, Greil Marcus, Dave Marsh—excelled in other genres as well. Though I played a decent piano and had been attending concerts since seeing The Doors at Hampton Beach Casino in New Hampshire, the older I got, the more I believed I didn't have the credentials to judge those performances.

Doomed to remain an outsider, sometimes I felt like an obligatory witness to a wedding performed at a justice of the peace office—never an actual participant in the joy and promise of that ceremony, or what would follow.

Then, I'd think of the night at Jonathan Swift's, a pub in Cambridge, when Jeffrey Newcomb, the bass player for Iron Dandelion, a band that had once filled concert venues worldwide, slammed his glass on the counter—following a gig less than one hundred people had attended, where he'd twice had to ask the bartender to lower the volume on the TV—and delivered a rant my way for not appreciating the privilege of being able to proselytize and for not recognizing how lucky I was to be "an apostle" of music, this "sacred art," before finally reminding me my job— recording the "scriptures with integrity"—mattered.

Though cocaine and alcohol fueled this tirade and there might've been more venom than reverence in his lecture—more terrified lament for the gifts he'd squandered than a desire to convert me—he struck a chord. I knew he believed every word or else he wouldn't still be performing in places like Swift's and dives much worse—his past royalties alone enough to fund any addictions he may have been battling.

So, I retooled my approach and envisioned my role as more historian and discoverer—sometimes nurturer and unabashed cheerleader of new talent.

I'd devoted several days to packing, yet my efforts had stalled. You'd assume with the countless moves over the last few years, I would have developed some sort of science for the task. At it late one night when the rising sun crept through the venetian blinds, I collapsed on my still-made bed—too bushed to pull open the covers.

A distant ring sounded in the background; muffled at first, it grew louder. In half sleep, I remembered I'd already packed my answering machine and tapes.

I fumbled for the handset—eyes closed.

"It's Johanna," a faint voice on the other end said.

"Who?"

"Johanna Beaumont. . . . From the Dylan concert?"

Grateful she contributed the qualifier; it saved me the embarrassment of asking her name again.

"Sure. Sure."

I opened one eye at last and rubbed sleep from the other. "How are you?"

"Great. . . . Listen, I want to invite you to an exhibition of my work at a small gallery. Near my studio. You doing anything next Thursday? . . . Wonderful," Johanna said. "It's in Avon."

Uncertain if she'd given me an opportunity to pause and reflect—or if I might've said "No," or "Nothing," in answer to her question—I scrambled to find a scrap of paper, snatched a red envelope that once held a card for my confirmation from the trash bucket, and scribbled down the gallery's address.

After I hung up the phone, my usual doubts sprung forth: I didn't even know her—she was a flake. What about that guy, Ted? Johanna was older than me—maybe considerably older.

So what? a voice from somewhere deep inside answered. I lay back down and grabbed a few more hours of sleep.

— 4 —

I caught up with Johanna, dressed in jeans and a blouse. A random array of hand-painted, thin magenta brush strokes covered both sides of her shirt; embroidered colored beads adorned its front. She apologized for her casual attire before loosening the knot of my tie and removing it.

"This first event is low-key—for gallery friends and a few generous donors. I've got a more formal change of clothes in the car for the *official opening*,"— she used her two hands to create air quotes—"which happens tonight. . . . You look fine, though."

I wanted to tell her she looked much more than fine. And should have said something in the vein of "exquisite" but processed the edit in time and stopped myself before uttering a word.

Johanna took me to her studio, one of a dozen or more housed in a long, narrow structure extending out behind the exhibition space. A mix of turpentine and charcoal ash odors filled the room. Works in progress sat on easels.

One, a mixed media canvas effort, appeared to be

row houses from a New York City street. A single window shone in bright yellow; the rest remained unlit. Storm clouds raged in turbulent motion and dark blues overhead. Another, a collage fixed on wood base, had embedded feathers and other artifacts—reminiscent of fossils—within it.

Several more pieces hung from a strip of guide wire strung on the back wall. A couple of tables lined the side; scattered atop them were pastel chalk, acrylic as well as oil tubes, paint rollers, and aerosol spray cans—along with myriad brushes of every shape and size. Windows faced a patch of woods bordering the arts center. Three strips of track lighting beamed down from the ceiling.

"It's only around five hundred square feet. And you're not supposed to sleep here. But I'm getting tired commuting to the pit,"—her term for New Haven. "Be nice to find someplace closer to live."

Thankful she finally secured a workspace, Johanna told me she would've loved to wake up and return to her efforts immediately, during that first cup of coffee, rather than after enduring the Route 91 commute battles that robbed her of momentum and drained her a little more each day. And, on those occasions when immersed in a project, the prospect of laboring into the wee hours and crashing on site—or at least nearby—would've been a godsend.

She and another resident artist who shared this show agreed on "Herstory" as their theme. They'd presented Johanna's pieces in one corner—mounting several on glossy white drywall while fixing others on the cinder block exterior.

I discovered from a plaque the building once operated as the Climax Fuse factory, where people from Poland, Russia, Italy, Germany, and other European nations arrived in Avon to assist in manufacturing. The company had even sent workers to New York to greet newly arriving immigrants and recruit them into the business. This structure's repurposing might've been the definitive example of replacing darkness and struggle with creativity and light.

Many of Johanna's works were mixed media, and a few included a variety of objects she'd retrieved: driftwood, pinecones, and autumn leaves. She mentioned artists like Duchamp and Chicago, and these references often stumped me.

Johanna spied my puzzled expression. "Don't worry. Just enjoy the work."

Easy for her to say, I thought. Hoping to be up for that day's challenge, I regretted not having performed a bit of research before my trip. I had a tendency to dwell too much inside my head, and these roadblocks arose especially if I ventured out of my comfort zone. It was as if certain neurotransmitters— ones that eased my capacity to accept joy and novel experiences—were blocked. Then—like a school crossing guard—my subconscious stepped in front of me and waved a massive stop sign. I wanted to— needed to—move forward but didn't know, or had forgotten, the rules of the road.

I hustled to grab a glass of cabernet, swiped a slice of cheese and cracker from the tray of a passing server, and wondered if I'd always be like this.

Johanna's approach to art—as well as life— seemed to offer a prescription for this stunted-growth condition of mine. She accompanied me around the gallery, pointed certain elements out— light, the use of color, the weight of brush strokes— and encouraged me to view things from a fresh per-spective. I eagerly awaited the opportunity to try.

That process started with baby steps though, and I didn't have Johanna's type of vision. I inspected a different painting—not hers—and took in the entire flower, its petals, the drops of morning dew—even the diverse nuances of red and yellow. I couldn't ex-plain it; Johanna had an ability to perceive these in-dividual components, not as separate entities, but as one life force.

23

"You're supposed to engage art with your heart—not your brain," Jo told me with a laugh. "Don't think. *Feel*." She gave me a mock tap on my head.

One of Johanna's works depicted the Iranian crisis: several skulls superimposed over a map of the desert washed in blood-like watercolors. Another featured a disturbing combination of female anatomical parts—breasts, vulva, pregnant bellies—literally sewn together in disjointed fashion with stitches of dark thread whose loose strands fell in various places outside the frame.

An electric mix of songs—predominantly by women—played through mounted ceiling speakers overhead while a dozen or more invited guests milled about, drank wine, and nibbled refreshments.

Tanya Tucker crooned a country ballad; Kate Bush offered a couple of angst-ridden pieces before those segued into folk-punk by Patti Smith, a new wave number by Debbie Harry, and the unvarnished soul of Whitney Houston. Later, Joan Jett and Chrissie Hynde belted out badass rock 'n' roll. Jackson Browne's "For A Dancer" and Dylan's "You're A Big Girl Now"—two token male songs—joined the rotation.

Johanna glided through the room like a face painter hired for a backyard celebration—an entertainer who kept smiling and maintained her composure even while demanding six-year-olds hovered.

I paused near an oversized painting of Johanna's—probably three by four feet. A tall man, dressed in suit coat and jeans, sporting an ascot, stopped beside me. "Quite de Kooning*esh*," he said. "Particularly in its level of abstract realism."

"Er, yeah . . ." I managed, after a lengthy interval.

To me, it looked similar to a modern-day version of *American Gothic,* except the featured couple were two women. What did I know? My frame of reference was less likely Grant Wood and more the New Country Cornflakes TV commercial I remembered seeing as a kid.

The guy stretched upright and did not budge—a screen actor who'd hit his mark and now stood poised to welcome the precise camera angle.

Then Johanna walked up—hors d'oeuvres in hand. She asked me to open wide and placed something wrapped with bacon in my mouth. I hated scallops; they could sometimes make me ill in fact. But I swallowed anyway.

"I've been able to discern how your work is in *hoooom*age to William de Kooning's *Woman 1*," the man said. "However, rather than an appropriation, your piece takes the subject to an innovational plane due to the preponderant monochromatism of its composition and tone . . . Grady Thomas."

He handed Johanna his business card.

I had no idea what the hell the guy was talking about. For the last few minutes, I'd only heard long fingernails scraping against a blackboard and couldn't find a method of escaping the classroom. I'd wondered who might've been worse off. Me, someone who knew too little. Or that professor-type who knew too much.

"Thank you," Johanna said politely. "Will you excuse us?"

She pulled me by the arm to a corner of the room, removed his card from her pocket and discretely threw it into a bucket along with her napkin and paper plate. "Hope *should* be the artist's currency and love her only ware," she said to me.

Once again, I didn't have a clue.

"Wanna get out of here?"

"Is it OK? Won't they miss you?"

She took my hand in hers and dragged me to the door before mentioning a state park—not more than a three-mile walk from there.

"Three miles?" I said—feigning outrage.

We carefully crossed busy Route 202 and headed towards Arch Road.

— 5 —

Long and winding, Arch Road had once hosted several more farms than those we passed that afternoon. We walked for only a few minutes before ending up in front of a church. If you caught its intricately crafted wooden sign at the right angle, you'd swear it read "The Church of SatAn"—because of the way a crucifix had been carved between the two 'n's of Anne and the overgrown evergreens obscuring it. The designer had also placed the *t* and *a* too close together. So, at first glance, Johanna and I mistakenly saw the word "Satan."

Jo pointed to a placard near the entranceway, then spun around. "My middle name! With an *e'*. "— something Anne of Green Gables might've blurted out in her search for a bosom friend. She clutched my arm and led me to the door.

The space differed markedly from the traditional

parishes of my altar boy—and early Franciscan prep school—days; though I hadn't stepped foot inside a church of any type for a number of years. Johanna's enthusiastic response surprised me. *Is she a "church" person?* I wondered.

"Isn't it incredibly bright?" Jo said.

"I guess."

It struck me as too linear. No, that wasn't the correct term. Carefully plotted?

Like religious doctrine, the building's architecture had been formulated by mathematical absolutes: Behavior A plus contrition B equaled Heaven.

High above the altar, apostles stood side-by-side; one held what appeared to be a real ax—another an actual sword. Could this have been an element that drew folks to the parish—a modern interpretation of scripture and design, the mixed media component of its sculptures? Still, as contemporary as this structure was, a remnant scent of incense pervaded the place.

A wedding scene portrayed in one of the stained glass windows—though more vivid—was not as multidimensional and layered as a piece of Johanna's in the gallery. Hers, titled *The Promise*, depicted a pastel portrait of a married couple staged in the stereotypical pose a hired photographer might attempt to capture immediately after the ceremony. But Johanna's groom gazed in the opposite direction of his bride, and the flowers she clung to steadfastly, crumbled and dissipated into wisps of cumulus clouds.

The pattern of green, blue, and yellow making up a different window brought to mind a work of hers in the exhibit. Created only with a roller, a half dozen naked women huddled close—not one looked at another. Painted predominantly in black and white, just a few splashes of color washed parts of each nude form. The optimistic interpreter in me wanted to believe though this group was together, they'd not yet bonded, and these colored stripes mirrored the ultimate potential of both a rainbow and those assembled. On further review however, I could understand how someone else might envision this composition as a depiction of Hell and its licks of color: flames.

We lit a votive candle and slipped a few dollars as an offertory in front of one more realistic icon—in this case, they armed Joseph with a hand-saw. Johanna bowed; I made a sign of the cross—despite any misgivings—and we headed for the exit.

Johanna turned and said—à propos of nothing—"You know. Saint Anne was Mary's mother."

I hadn't remembered; "Hmmm" was the only thing I could say.

Across the parking lot, a handwritten notice affixed to a stake informed us a garden plot was being tilled for the parish's food bank. A nearby electric fountain gurgled and circulated water in a small cement pond dotted with weeds that peeked out from a few fissures.

Johanna took my hand again, and we hiked down the road.

Two kids around seven—possibly brother and sister—scurried past on bicycles. Following several yards behind, a woman pushed a baby carriage and nodded.

"I was married," Johanna said—eyes staring straight ahead. "A dentist. Some pieces in the show are from that period. Most of them done in Provence."

"I didn't know you studied in France." Of course, the bigger surprise and more likely and apt response should have been, "I didn't know you had a husband."

Then again, how could I have? This was only the second time we'd been together. To demonstrate that I'd been listening intently—more importantly, that I cared—I should've mentioned her marriage. Why did I think I had to validate my concern? Didn't the fact I'd taken the day off, driven one and a half hours to Connecticut, confirm my interest? Would it matter? What about Ted?

"I called it my *dark* phase. Presumptuous of me, huh? To suppose my career so far had already earned the status of defined periods."

A few passing cars whished by; the lonesome notes of a train horn echoed softly in the background.

"Decent man. But a traditionalist. He pictured me in a different frame. Everything seemed fine— charming home in Wisconsin, food on the table. Friends I knew would've been content. I sounded so selfish, wanting more. Not *more* actually, I guess, something . . . *else*. I begged him to let me put a studio in the space above our garage. But he got jealous. . . . Was it jealousy? I'm not sure now . . . Maybe impatience? He'd sometimes go into these rages. Little ones. Scary. Because I wouldn't stay in the box he constructed. The me he saw—the *us* he envisioned."

Johanna delivered each sentence in measured fashion—with several marked pauses between them—as if a filtering process might've been taking place; I hadn't heard her speak that way before.

"I wanted a family at some point. Robbie wasn't enthused; I was never clear where he stood." Her voice trailed off. "Those matters . . . aren't always in your hands."

"I'm sorry." I stopped our stroll to caress her arm.

She looked at me, shook her head, and we walked once again.

"I heard about an art fellowship in Provence. Got accepted and flew to France. In the beginning, those bleak works reflected loss . . . the dissolution of our marriage."

The double jingle of a metal bell rang and the two kids passed on their return trip.

Johanna told me about an afternoon, some weeks after her arrival in France. She'd hopped off her bike, edged towards a rocky cliff, and marveled at a sky awash in yellow and orange. Larks warbled; lavender scents made their way from the fields below, and she felt "emancipated."

"I realized I'd been granted a second chance. But, at the same time . . ." Johanna paused before turning to look at me. "Did you ever have a day, so delightful, so serene—yet so magnificent—that you somehow realize you'll never top it again? As if you'd been given a cake so spectacular you dreaded cutting into it?"

I couldn't be certain if Johanna was still speaking about France.

She reached up, ripped a single maple leaf from a low-hanging branch, then painstakingly separated it from the veins. "Do you have any idea how devastating it can be when each of you spends most of your waking hours desperately trying to prove you're not someone—when afterwards you discover that's precisely who you really are in the first place?"

$-6-$

We walked in purposeful silence until we stood before a white clapboard building with black shutters. Window boxes, sporting colored flowers and overflowing vines, welcomed us to Miller's Farm General Store.

"Let's have a picnic," Johanna said, her tone exuberant.

She didn't seem to be a picnic person to me.

I had no option but to oblige. So, I held open the door for her; the screen closed with a loud snap behind us when I let go too soon.

The largest chalkboard I'd ever seen—crammed with handwritten prices and exotic specials featuring venison, rabbit, turkey heart, duck feet, and wild boar—hung on a long wall to the right. I gleaned from their takeout menu the store—established in 1950, primarily as a poultry farm—had diversified. Baskets of fresh produce—tomatoes, cukes, lettuce, squash—lined the perimeter of the room. Lemon scents rose from herbs. Apple cider, chocolate milk, and bottled water rested in a glass-door-enclosed fridge. Wine produced at local vineyards, along with canned and boxed staples—mostly those used to prepare stuffing—sat on a few shelves.

The beverage refrigerator's compressor kicked on, rumbled and competed with *pat, pat, pat,* sounds of someone chopping on a block in a back section of the floor. Johanna picked up a Miller Turkey Brining Kit from one shelf and read its ingredients.

The pounding ceased. A middle-aged woman, dressed in an apron embroidered with an image of a chicken and the phrase *Where Everyone Is Family,* approached the counter and smiled. She rung up our order of turkey sandwiches, pickles, and a bottle of wine, then stuffed several napkins, cups, and paper plates into the bag, and we headed for the exit. Before leaving, Johanna spied apples in a wicker basket hanging from the ceiling. She grabbed a couple and when she turned around to pay for them, the woman waved her off.

A crushed-stone path led to a wide meadow with a few mildly sloped, slightly rolling hills and three picnic tables strategically placed.

"There." Johanna pointed to the one furthest

away and closest to the edge of the woods.

"Do I have a choice?" I grinned.

We arranged things on the table, and I poured the Merlot.

An uncle, who I loved, was raised an hour from where Johanna grew up. His dairy farm sprawled over hundreds of acres in Fond du Lac, a community on the south end of Lake Winnebago. Though I'd only visited the place once when very young, over the years, aunts, uncles—as well as my parents—discussed the serenity and joy of this homestead. Yet, on the few occasions Uncle Ed shared stories describing the efforts of his dad and his own uncles, it seemed those positive experiences were coupled with a great deal of toil and hardship.

My uncle later moved to New England in the late 1960s to work as an engineer, but his soft-spoken tales—of chores, classes in a one-room schoolhouse, touch football games with his brothers and the pastoral settings they took place in—formed my only impression of his home state. So I said to Johanna, "All of this must be familiar to you, since you're from Wisconsin," before gesturing towards an expanse of lush undulating slopes and a few cows grazing in a lower field.

"You kidding me?" Johanna laughed, coughed a

bit, and spit out sips of wine. "Far from it. Appleton is the paper-mill capital of the state. Towns nearby could be called scenic, I guess. What I remember is concrete, gas stations, and the sulfur stench from pulp—I couldn't wait to get out. No—"

Sorry I'd broached the subject and ready to say so, Johanna halted mid-sentence, as if by libeling her hometown she'd committed a treacherous act and now hoped to make amends.

"A lot of teachers encouraged me—especially Sister Teresa in English class, who reminded us of the power and potential strength of women. Not exactly indoctrination, but it stuck for sure. Strange, since she lived such a cloistered existence herself."

"Maybe that was the point, though—her motivation to reach you."

"Those encouragements were rare. As early as Jefferson elementary, I stared out the window, watched trains rumble by. Like Francie in *A Tree Grows in Brooklyn*—I thought there's *got* to be someplace better for me."

Johanna looked at the fields. "There weren't pastures—or much vegetation of any kind—in my neighborhood, anyway. If you didn't count those enormous polyester plants guarding the main entrance to Outagamie Bank. So, I'd slip away to Riverside cemetery—and its patch of woods—not far from my house."

She told me about a slight bluff that bordered the graveyard, sloped down to railroad tracks below, and formed the banks of the Fox River.

"Freight trains, loaded with paper and other stuff from the mills, slowed to a crawl at the bend. Guys jumped onto a box or flat car and headed north to Green Bay or south to Madison. I knew I somehow had to escape as well."

"It couldn't have been that rough." Although, how could I know? "I bet you drove the nuns crazy."

"Just the opposite. I joined every activity I could. National Honor Society, Drama Club—*and* the Legionnette drill team. Can you believe it?"

When she spoke, Johanna's eyes shone bright, welcoming, and steady—as if teaching a classroom of eager students, and the lesson for that day had been the discovery of a new world or miracle drug, rather than an account of her alienated teenage years.

The activities she took part in during high school appeared to be a four-year shopping spree, where she'd placed everything of interest in her cart. Those experiences—even the difficult ones somehow—still continued to nourish her soul. While, if I were honest, most of that period remained a blur to me, with my former classmates' questions of "Remember when?" met with blank stares.

Johanna spoke of one nun in particular, Sister Mary Ellen, who unceasingly buoyed her. Of a pen-and-ink drawing with a train rounding the bend by the river washed in light purple watercolor. Her teacher—unbeknownst to Johanna—entered the piece in a regional art contest, and it earned first prize.

"That marked the beginning of my purple phase." Then she performed a near perfect imitation of an NPR narrator's voice. "Johanna Beaumont's career began very early in the back hills of Wisconsin."

She laughed, and the winter squall of dread trying its best to sneak up on me—despite how well the day had been going—retreated.

"Had to be tough if the lushest spot you could find was the cemetery."

"That's an exaggeration. But hey, don't knock graveyards. The site teemed with wildlife. Rabbits, flying squirrels, songbirds . . .

"I lost my virginity there," she said in a whisper. "Next to the headstone of Kate Blood—a supposed witch. I hung out a lot on that side of the cemetery— almost in the woods. The stories were stupid and vile—*she was an ax murderer; blood trickled from her*

39

tombstone. I felt bad and wanted to keep her company. Every year, the bakeries in town would even sell "Kitty" Halloween cookies. Her nickname. She got TB, and they sent her to Kansas—hoping she'd recover. But, before long, a train carried her body home to Appleton . . . Only twenty-three, she left a two-year-old daughter behind. That never stopped people from saying those despicable things."

Johanna scraped the blade of her plastic knife back and forth repeatedly along the picnic table's edge. Our conversation reminded me of my introductory French classes in tenth grade when each "*bonjour*"—and every new word that followed—was delightfully enhanced by the flair of rookie instructor Miss Barshinger. Johanna dropped *g*'s at the end of words so they sounded like *tryin* and *likin*. And the manner in which she closed her statements with a rising inflection—as if they might be questions— brought with it a certain level of humility and savoir-faire at the same time.

Johanna's Civics teacher recommended she prepare a senior-year project based on Kate Blood.

"Sister Xavier would have been mortified if she knew just *how* intimately I'd been connected to that section of the cemetery."

A few months later, that same nun surrendered

her prized ticket—there were less than 400 available—to a Martin Luther King Jr. event at the Fox Valley Center and gave it to Johanna.

"Dr. King denounced the War and said he wouldn't limit his morals to a single area of his life—restrict them to civil rights alone. Wherever he saw immorality, he would take a stand. And I got so charged up then.

"Neo-Nazis brandished *Let your people GO* signs. Disturbing because these protestors weren't only old white men and women, many were students and young—the same as me. So I vowed to leave in three weeks—after graduation—join CORE and head south to help with voter registration drives. I lost my nerve. Took years to get out of town. Went to college in Madison. Married a dentist. Wimped out . . . Safe, safe, safe."

Johanna snapped the knife in two—piercing the skin of her hand.

I grabbed a napkin and pressed it to her palm. "You *are* brave. You left and traveled. Look at what you've accomplished—"

"—Yeah. Some teaching. Half a dozen exhibitions at small galleries—most of them joint shows." She tossed the napkin into the paper bag along with the others, then stood and dusted herself off.

41

"Shut up," I said, sterner than I'd intended. From the little I'd ascertained about the art world, I understood this much: Johanna was more than gifted.

"Chill." She smiled good-naturedly—unfazed by my anger.

Johanna gazed at treetops bordering the field and told me of days she'd practice sketching by focusing on a couple of birches—the only trees on their property. "Side-by-side, two trunks sprouted, then separated. Their branches joined and circled each other at the top. Like an embrace. You couldn't make out a patch of sky through those leaves . . . Sorry. Have no idea what prompted that—got to pee."

She walked towards the woods and disappeared. After a few minutes, I spied her picking flowers in the meadow.

I scooched over to a nearby tree, leaned against it, and watched Johanna before taking out a notebook and scribbling down a few reflections. Snippets of the day's experiences I hoped to capture and process before they were lost. How lucky she'd been to see Martin Luther King in person and only a town over from Appleton—which Johanna later shared was "one of the last sundown cities for God's sake."

I pondered MLK's courage, and Johanna's. Having now learned the year she graduated from high school, I realized I could calculate her age. Seven years older than me wasn't too terrible, I reasoned.

I stopped writing and sketched. Primitive, the drawing began with a gravestone. Johanna's profile peeked out from behind—as best as I could appropriate it—along with her bare breast.

"Stop that."

Johanna startled me.

Daffodils and tulips in one hand, she snatched my notebook and flung it away with her other. "There's a time to live and a time to record."

She surprised me with a kiss full on the lips before grabbing my arm and helping me up.

"What's that?" Jo noticed a red mark on my left hand near the wrist.

"Nothing."

I picked up the notebook, closed it, then reached for her hand and headed to the crushed-stone road.

We reached a large paddock. Johanna emitted a rapid *click, click, click* sound from the side of her mouth and a brown horse with splashes of white approached. From her jacket pocket, she took out an apple we got at the General Store; then pulled a small Swiss Army knife from her jeans. Though intrigued by this gadget, I'd promised myself I'd stop questioning her. Johanna sliced the apple into pieces, stuck her hand out, and the horse chomped the fruit greedily. Within minutes, nothing remained but Johanna's wet fingers, which she— summarily and without apology—dried by rubbing them on my slacks.

"Let's go for a ride," she said.

While I *could* envision Johanna horseback riding; the idea of me on top of a saddle was another story. Besides, I wasn't dressed for the occasion.

Years before, at a ranch in Wyoming, I waited in

line to rent a horse while they asked the person in front of me if she was an experienced rider. After the young women said, "No. Not really," they found a gentler steed for her. When they posed the same question to me, I told them my skills were also limited; the staff searched in vain for a different mount.

"You'll be fine," the lanky, cattle-roping Sam Shepard stand-in with cowboy hat said before handing over the reins to the stallion he'd deemed too spirited for the woman. In short order, King George reared up on his hind legs three separate times—like the scene from the opening credits of *The Lone Ranger*—and we'd only covered a quarter mile of the path to that point. I hung on and did my best to turn him around—heading in the direction where he intended to go anyway—then returned to the stall.

I hadn't been on one since.

Too late to change her mind, Johanna had already chosen hers, given the bunch of flowers she'd picked in the field to the cashier, and was preparing to mount.

A ranch hand helped me position, and I strained to keep balance by planting my feet snug inside the stirrups. Johanna gently squeezed the flanks of her horse with her legs and sped off.

"Watch out for bears!" the man called out before

we entered the woods. "We haven't seen any—but Fox61 reported sightings in backyards a few streets over."

This tidbit did wonders for my anxiety.

By then a distance away, Jo deliberately steered towards felled logs and stone-wall sized boulders bordering the path. Horse and rider leapt and pounced in such fury that I wondered if a frenzied spirit had hijacked the woman I'd just picnicked with.

Johanna headed straight for a couple of dangling pine branches. "Careful. Slow down!" But she hadn't heard—or ignored—my shouts, ducked, then slipped to the horse's side. Holding on with one hand, she laughed uncontrollably.

My fear reminded me of the time I watched a teenaged-girl fall from a pony and slide out of reach on the Hippodrome carousel at Revere Beach. She seemed more concerned about keeping her summer dress tight against her tanned and sculpted thighs than tumbling into the churning gears at the center of that clamorous merry-go-round.

I finally drew closer. Johanna tugged the reins and allowed me to catch up. "Could have killed yourself."

She gasped for breath, then grinned before we

settled into a comfortable trot.

After a while, the other riders thinned out, leaving only Johanna and me on the path. Thank God for the marked trails. Hopeless out there, I regretted not taking a map from the rack hanging on their barn wall. Valley Hill Equestrian advertised over two hundred acres of trails. They meandered through thick woodlands, in sharp contrast to the only ones I'd ever run—or sometimes ridden a bike on—which were converted railroad beds: staked out and abundantly clear.

Somehow, Johanna gained confidence the deeper we ventured. Further and further we roamed—the occasional chipmunk, squirrel, or chickadee, our only companions. The forest was in full bloom, scented with the spice of fallen pine needles and fecund damp earth. But splashes of orange and red hinted at autumn.

The *cloppity clop, cloppity clop* of eight hooves progressively segued into a chorus of four. Leaf litter swished, crinkled, and sloshed like soft brush strokes on a snare drum. Sunlight streaked intermittently through a dense mix of conifer, beech, maple, and birch, and skimmed across sections of woods. Peripheral and perpendicular paths in various states of clearing crossed one another—lumber routes scarcely worked, trails no longer in use—until the forest revealed an expanse of open meadow. Hundreds of yards ahead stood an outcrop of boulders; a body of water, a brook wide as a large pond—maybe a lake—appeared on the right.

The late afternoon sun set slowly behind us. Shadows danced atop blades of tall grass caressed by a desultory wind. I had little interest in stirring from this reverie, hoping—as a student does on a school day—that I could rest my head on the pillow, return to my dreams, and never wake.

Johanna and I veered towards the brook, stopped, and exhaled in tandem. A sense of relief, a stillness—feelings not experienced in a very long time—overcame me. Other than a thrush pining for his mate and a sole angler casting his line on the distant side of the water, we were alone.

We rode our horses closer to the edge. I looked at the fisherman, then down to watch a single leaf float by—like the past I didn't want to remember, even if impossible to forget.

Lack of conversation usually made me anxious; yet, I hadn't felt the need to offer Johanna a running commentary providing insights to a particular rare bittern indigenous to the region—or a species of cattail that bloomed in the area—simply to fill the silence.

I tried to let things be.

After riding about a half mile beyond the eastside of the brook, the end of a corral came into view— which meant the trail we'd been on was horseshoe-shaped and we weren't far from our starting point.

"Sorry Matt. It's getting dark. We're not gonna be able to visit that state park today. We'd never get back in time."

I wasn't disappointed.

"There's a lesson here somewhere," Johanna said.

"What's that?

"Oh, I don't know. Maybe it's best not to map out every detail?"

— 8 —

Johanna took my hand, and we hustled towards the gallery. Traffic stalled at a stop sign where the street met Route 202 and a railway crossed overhead. She tugged me in the direction of a steeply sloped embankment bordering the bridge's left side. We struggled to the crest—Johanna never once let me go—even though both of us nearly lost our balance twice.

I walked past a cement mile marker that had to be close to one hundred years old or more and reflected on the many journeys it must've borne witness to.

Stubborn tufts of grass sprouted alongside creosote-stained ties and dull, unvarnished rails. The sight saddened me. Though, the train line hadn't yet been abandoned, it would only be a matter of time. The smell of tar hearkened back to grammar school and the days I'd place pennies on Boston & Maine tracks waiting for them to be flattened by the potent Buddliners that cruised by St. Mary's.

A whippoorwill sang while Johanna skirted the tracks in search of—God knows what. The ground vibrated; a flock of sparrows several yards away scattered at the sound of two distant whistle blasts. Bells from a nearby crossing gate clanged. Johanna didn't move quickly enough in my estimation; so I yanked her from the rails. When a rust-colored locomotive chugged around the bend, the engineer waved, sounded the whistle again, and passed by. Boxcars from Forestville and County Lumber rumbled along, featuring sides plastered with the names of Clark Brothers Bolt, Levitz Furniture, and Lecsade Kitchens. After perhaps three dozen cars, I was thrilled to spot a real caboose and not just some large flashing red light affixed to the rear of a box or flat car. A brakeman emerged, placed one hand on the railing and half waved with the other.

The decrescendo refrain of *clickity-clicks* echoed until the freight vanished from view.

I clung to Johanna, and we slid down the steep slope—kicking dirt in every direction. She locked her arm in mine and we trekked across the perilous 202 to reach the Arts Center. As we strode up the driveway, a figure appeared from the corner of my eye and headed our way.

"Ted. What are you doing here?" Johanna said, then extricated herself from me.

"They've canceled the last couple stops of the tour."

"Well . . . that's good news." She hugged his neck. "Can you guys excuse me? It's late, and I gotta change for tonight's reception."

"Sure," we said before awkwardly looking at each other.

Ted turned away first by facing the road.

I scuffed the bottom of my sneaker on the hot top, attempting to remove a few pebbles. They'd most likely gotten lodged from gravel spread on the railway bed or from a crushed-stone path we'd strolled on earlier. I fixed my eyes on Johanna's back. She disappeared behind a screen door—a hanger full of clothes she'd hauled from the trunk of her car draped over her shoulder.

"Lot of traffic." Ted twisted his body to look at me.

I stuck my hand halfway forward as if to offer a handshake.

For a moment, Ted moved his in my direction and then stopped before—as nonchalantly as possible—placing it inside his pants pocket.

Recovering in time, I slipped my fingers through my hair.

Brakes screeched on 202. Someone leaned on a horn and kept it there. Another person yelled, "Asshole!"

Ted smiled.

I shook my head at the unfolding rush-hour scene.

"So . . . You're in a band?" I said.

In the painful small talk that followed, I learned Ted was a bassist in a group that had recently opened on the East Coast leg of Bob Seger's tour. And, after having achieved a modicum of success and a number of glowing reviews, their manager thought it shrewd to send them out on their own. Far too soon as it turned out. No doubt the guy believed twenty-five percent of a headlining gig made more sense at that juncture for *him* than whatever percentage he'd been earning from their opening-act sets. So, with little promotion and next to no advance work, Ted would end up swiping hors d'oeuvres from the gallery table.

As much as I planned to, *needed* to, dislike Ted, he didn't seem to be a bad person. He loved "On the Nickel" and "Hearts of Stone," deep cuts from Waits and Springsteen, and was as incredulous as me everyone mentioned *After the Gold Rush* when listing Neil Young masterpiece albums but overlooked *Everybody Knows This Is Nowhere*. Ted knew Al Kooper played French horn on the Stones' hit "You Can't Always Get What You Want" and Jerry Garcia backed Crosby, Stills, and Nash on pedal steel during "Teach Your Children." He pronounced the Corona and slice of lime trend overtaking the beer-drinking world sacrilegious—after all, what could beat an ungarnished Heineken? And, despite what *BillBoard* and *Rolling Stone* might say, no one could convince us Bob Seger ever wrote a better song than "Roll Me Away."

We entered the gallery.

Johanna mingled through the crowd. The edges of her sheer pastel-colored dress rippled as she fluttered from person to person—a Monarch butterfly in garden flight—resting her hand on one visitor, kissing the cheek of another. An ache rolled through me until it surged in my throat. Confused by the sharp, stabbing jabs that shot through my lower back like punches to the kidneys, I might've doubled over if Ted hadn't been standing beside me. *Weren't we supposed to experience devastation in the "pit of our stomachs?"*

"Excuse me," I said in the middle of an explanation he'd been delivering on his version of the bass line to "The Chain," a Fleetwood Mac tune. Instead of heading for the men's room though, I fumbled for the keys in my slacks and edged my way towards my car, Route 84, and the Mass Pike.

When I reached the Charlton Rest area—the halfway home point in my mind—I pulled in and bought a coffee, then walked to the outskirts of the parking lot, sat at a picnic table, and stared into the dark woods.

— 9 —

Some weeks passed before I got a rambling letter from Johanna, who chided me for leaving that day without saying goodbye. Though she didn't apologize for Ted's appearance—Jo let me know me she hadn't expected him. An upcoming job opportunity at Phillips Andover Academy became her new focus.

"Round hole. Square peg" was how Johanna referred to the possibility of a match between her and Andover. But, "if nothing else," she looked forward to the chance to spend an afternoon in the school's Addison Gallery after her interview. The Addison, Johanna informed me, housed originals of Hopper, Pollock, Cassatt, and Winslow Homer.

Her note—absent a hint of a request to be put up during her stay—included a proposed itinerary along with the statement "Plane arrives at Logan from Bridgeport at 7 p.m."

I'd been too sheep-faced to tell her about my

temporary lodging status; so Johanna hadn't a clue the Chelsea pad would no longer be an option. These living arrangements reinforced the differences between us. Yet, I hadn't wanted her to make other plans—no matter how embarrassing it might've proven.

Jo once told me she hated driving, avoided it when possible, and wasn't keen on being a passenger either—hence the flight. A tiny part of me felt peeved and somewhat taken advantage of. Did Johanna believe her time more valuable than mine?

Of course, my social calendar hadn't been booked that week—or for the next several. Who had I been hoping to fool? Ecstatic, I anxiously awaited her visit.

In order to move into mom's house and be ready for Johanna, I'd have to leave the apartment days ahead of my original plan. The many boxes stacked against the walls and the ton of stuff—clothes, books, record albums—still not packed, made this seem a nearly impossible task. So I called Johanna a number of times and left a few messages with her roommates, but didn't hear from her. I wasn't sure if she'd received them and ignored me or if they'd even passed on the information. In a panic, I reached out to my brother Orlando and pleaded with him to take a day off from the gas station to help.

Revere

— 10 —

Revere, the city where I was raised and where my mother still lived, is located one town north of Boston. The Atlantic Ocean forms a border to the east. Established in 1895, its three-mile stretch of sandy shore is purported to be the nation's first public beach. From the turn of the century until the 1970s, an amusement park flourished on the boardwalk—with Ferris wheels, dodgem cars, movie theaters, carousels, roller coasters, clam shacks, hot dog and frozen custard stands, dance halls, and haunted houses. Only vestiges of those structures survived; most had either burned down, were boarded up, or had been demolished.

In Revere's heyday, several members of organized crime—the Mafia or the Mob, as they were called then—took advantage of the city's horse and greyhound racetracks and its countless nightclubs as well as its proximity to Boston. They extended their tentacles throughout the community, contaminating it while stigmatizing the majority of regular, law-abiding citizens.

Most Revere natives kept silent about these associations—certainly the people I'd come in contact with while growing up. A pathogen, that underworld agent permeated the town's cells and sometimes prevailed. As a result, the municipality's original identity as a place founded and operated by hardworking immigrants was destroyed—or, at the very least, severely damaged.

In much the same manner as you might fail to acknowledge your Uncle Roberto when he snuck that extra nip or two after supper, or Mrs. Rittorosi's overnight excursions down the street to Paul Donovan's bed on the nights his wife worked part-time at the Schrafft's candy factory in Charlestown, or the stack of "dirty" magazines your gang of friends hid between the crevices of an old stone wall running along the edge of the "Indian Trail"—a sliver of woods bordering our neighborhood—nearly all the folks in town practiced the tenets of denial in their own unique ways. In most circumstances, this became a fool's errand.

Few who resided beyond our city made any attempt to sugarcoat the facts about organized crime here—especially the three major Boston newspapers of that era. And, even a decade or so later, it was a rare instance when I could bring up my hometown—or be asked to spell my last name—without someone referring to the Mafia.

As the honorable men and women of the greatest generation came home from World War Two settled in, built ranches, Capes, the occasional colonial, and painstakingly labored to put food on the table, and as family neighborhoods sprouted, thugs—and worse—proliferated. Sure, some typically harmless "numbers runners" remained content in that station for the rest of their lives. But others rose the ladder to different, more severe roles by getting involved in "protection"—shaking businesses down and forcing them to pay "insurance"—or by selling hot stuff: televisions, radios, and other appliances that somehow "fell off a truck." These apprenticeships led many participants to become pimps, enforcement soldiers, *capos*, or something equally dangerous.

Yet, if you were to drive through this community back then on trips to and from Boston, there'd be little chance of witnessing the underlying decay. Like Mr. Donovan's bedroom exploits, this criminal activity—along with collective guilt—spread behind closed doors. Beat cops ignored the illegal gambling that transpired in pool halls and barber shops, officers from the area's state trooper barracks parked their cruisers in front of a "stuffed animal" shop at the corner of Broadway and Shore Road to buy fenced goods, and the police chief's grandson worked all summer at a beach amusement establishment purported to be owned by an underworld operative. Given all this, who would rake through the debris of our town to uncover the blight spreading and choking lives in its path—never mind make efforts to destroy it?

Local politicians railed histrionically at front-page stories about district crime in tabloids like the *Record American* or the more respectable rags: the *Herald Traveler* and *Boston Globe*. While other residents also grew upset by these headlines and feature articles, they'd only complain about the unfair portrayals of the city and its inhabitants among themselves and then return to their jobs the following day with resignation. These people—including my shoe-factory-laborer grandfather who had pored over newspapers each evening to overcome his broken English—toiled, hoping to attain a better life—perhaps even one that ensued outside the confines of Revere's borders. But assimilation to first- and second-generation immigrants was indelibly linked to "not making trouble."

Complicated to be sure, I hadn't seriously considered the role geography played in a person's development until long after I'd moved out. I'm not certain what behavior I'd expected of the inherently decent citizens and relatives who inhabited most of my city. It seemed to me—in those days at least—there were only two codes of conduct for a man raised in Revere. Just two paths to choose. Both of which demanded silence, loyalty, and a particular type of sucking up as their prerequisites. Sometimes these paths converged, rendering a conundrum. What was I to make of the "leg breaker" when he was also the same person who walked the aisles of Saint Mary's with a collection basket during the Mass offertory and the first to bring groceries to the house when your non "connected" uncle died from a sudden heart attack at fifty-three?

To this day, I wonder if my older cousin Vinnie—who lived across the street from me and ate supper at our table most Saturdays—struggled with this same confused concept of masculinity before he joined the Marines, shipped off to a place called Khe Sanh, and never came back. Or, what Orlando's best friend Arthur thought about the topic after he did come home from Nam but never really returned to us.

I came to understand a person's—and a city's—

history is spun into a tightly woven cloth of myth and reality, and we could never fully separate truth from fable.

Intrinsic to our makeup, we kids learned to play our part in this conspiracy of silence. So, at thirteen, when Sheila Giannino said her father was in the Mob—and her body shook any time a dark-colored car drove by on those nights we shared gulps from a gallon of Fortissimo wine in the Louis Pasteur schoolyard—most chose not to believe her, though her shaking could more accurately be defined as convulsions. It was easier and less painful that way. Some claimed Sheila sought attention. Even then, I knew how bizarre an accusation that had been. Others argued she'd flipped out. Although denying a woman's ache and voice was the norm, I've never been certain why we weren't capable of giving Sheila and her narrative—more importantly, her fear—credence.

The terror in Sheila's eyes no act, her anxiety exacerbated each successive night with every passing car.

If any of us had bothered to look at the Boston dailies, we would have noticed pictures of Sheila's dad and more splattered throughout them because of an ongoing trial that featured mobster Gerry Angiulo and Joseph Barboza Barron as its star witness. But how many kids read the paper at age thirteen—even if you delivered them in the morning before school as I had? And it was a fluke when our parents remembered the first names of our friends—never mind their last.

The few times I walked Sheila home after an evening out with the gang, she'd urge me to stop at the end of her short driveway.

I never asked why.

Dolphin Avenue—which usually evoked scenes from the upbeat *Flipper* TV show whenever I set foot on it—seemed to be an unlikely spot for the Mafia to hang out.

The Giannino house, a split ranch with a one-car garage, wasn't anything special. On the few occasions when I ran into her father—sullen and moody, washing his Buick with a garden hose or rolling up trash barrels from the curbside—I'm not sure he ever cracked a smile. Sheila would give him a quick embrace before running inside to greet her mother, and I don't remember a single word uttered in my direction. Nothing out of the ordinary struck me about him: just one more dad who didn't get enthused at the idea of a boy—any boy—with his teenage daughter.

On a Sunday in late December, after serving as altar boy for an overly long 10:15 High Mass at Our Lady of Lourdes Church, I bounded down the twenty steps, whizzed past the life-sized plastic nativity display, to a cart where twin brothers sold newspapers, and bought a *Globe* for my mom.

There, on its front-page, was a picture of Bernard A. Giannino, Sheila's father, beneath a headline which read "SHOT THREE TIMES IN THE BACK OF THE HEAD AT REVERE BEACH."

Confronted with an urban allegory stripped of its sheen, it would be years before I accepted that lesson's full force and truth.

Johanna had grown up believing in a better life somewhere else as she watched trains in Appleton round the bend and disappear. What had kept me anchored to Revere and stifled my ability to dream?

Whenever I saw a Hollywood advertisement for movies like *The Godfather* that glorified Mob members, or if I ventured—by accident—into pubs that employed mobster-theme stereotypes and props, or remembered the smug smirk on some lower mafia soldier's face strutting into Buonopane's grocery store to snitch an apple or a carton of cigarettes without fear of retribution, I'd think of Sheila, her robbed childhood, her younger brother and sister, and grow angry all over again.

Other memories surfaced—including a haircut I got when I was around eleven or twelve. Afterwards, I passed the alley between Joe the Barber's and the five-and-dime and came upon two men punching a hunched-over Mr. Doherty. When I headed a few steps in their direction, it surprised them and they stopped. One lifted Mister D a little while the other brushed imaginary dust from his shoulders.

"Are you OK?" I asked.

"I'm fine, Matt. Go home." He struggled to catch his breath.

I knew I should have run for help, but froze.

"Scram, kid," one guy said.

They apparently mistook my fright for balls. When I couldn't budge, they slammed Mr. Doherty against the barbershop's brick wall before swaggering off and saying, "This ain't over."

I wanted to do something for Mister D; but once more, he insisted I leave.

A few months later, his son Adam—a couple of grades ahead of me—let us know his father hadn't shown up for supper one night, and hadn't been heard from since.

I never told my friend—never told anyone—about that afternoon in the alley, and for years wondered if I'd done everything I could have, or had merely acted out the scene as it was supposed to be played according to the defined Revere script.

— 11 —

While Sheila Giannino dressed in the hip fashions of the era—including those gossamer blouses that drove boys wild—Heather, another friend, bore little resemblance to the delicate flower she was named after. Rather, she reminded me of the scrawny sticker bushes with their pesky seed pods that clung steadfastly to our clothes during walks on the Indian Trail.

She'd end up having dinner at my house a few nights a week because my mom just couldn't turn her away. We'd been friends for more than a year before I finally saw the apartment where she lived—purely by accident and not because of any invitation—Heather owned the gang's only catcher's mitt. Rug remnants that might have been discarded from the outlet store near the tracks on the Chelsea line—had they not been so dingy and discolored—covered her floors. You needed a wrench to twist her kitchen sink faucets on and off, and a perpetual chill haunted the rooms—no matter what the season. That first time in her place, I bumped into a boyfriend of her mother—one of several that paraded through. "Papa Charlie," "Daddy Glen," or some other silly moniker, according to Heather. I also learned babies were sometimes breastfed out of necessity and not simply for bonding reasons, or because of some modern-day doctrine stripped from the pages of the latest Yuppie handbook.

Heather—incessantly underfoot and a pest—insisted on following us guys around. We soon realized we wouldn't shake her, so I guess tolerance became the operative word—although I'm not sure we ever fashioned a conscious strategy for dealing with Heather. That she had a better baseball card collection than mine, hated Dylan, but loved Chicago and The Who, didn't help to endear her to me.

One afternoon Scott, Vernon, Damian, and I were hanging out at the Indian Trail, drooling over a recent *Penthouse,* when out from behind an evergreen popped Heather—her perennial Yankee cap placed annoyingly backwards on top of her head.

Damian—crass and ornery—whose father had died from cirrhosis and whose mother was having an affair with the landlord, and who invariably thought he had to prove something, turned the magazine round and let the glossy centerfold fall open to shock Heather, who, I surmised, had already seen plenty of this stuff play out in real life by her mother's drunken litany of boyfriends.

"What's the big deal?" she said, not missing a beat. "Everyone has them."

"Yeah?" Damian said. "So where the fuck are yours?"

His words and ensuing laugh were delivered with such venom I felt the sting myself.

I realized much later that Heather wanted the option to do everything a boy could and was convinced she had that right.

Typically the only girl on the diamond during pickup games at Frederick's Park, her Yankee cap pissed me off. Damian, Vernon, and some other kids refused to let her play initially, but their complaints didn't land because, to be honest, she was by far the best shortstop we had.

Heather likely considered her existence insignificant compared to other girls that age. How could she compete? By then, most of her classmates were sneaking out of their homes and putting on lipstick and makeup before school—or applying it after supper on our treks to the Pasteur school yard. I struggled to imagine Heather being at a hairdresser's—her hair habitually snarled whenever we hung out; yet somehow she managed to carry it off.

And, without a doubt, Heather had the most stunning brown eyes I'd ever seen. An indelible profundity emanated from them. The closest comparison I could think of were the Hummel characters featured in the gift section of Wolfson's Pharmacy. In that series of figurines and cards, the heads of the young girls were more exaggerated than the rest of their bodies, and their mournfully sympathetic brown, blue, and green eyes larger still. Later, when I got a job at that drugstore's soda fountain, I remember a few customers referring to those images with affection as part of the "big-eyed" collection.

After Damian spat out his insult, Heather had retreated to a tree several yards away. She leaned against it and frantically puffed on a Winston; her eyes—the ones I'd forever be enamored with—glistened.

I wandered over. "Nobody pays attention to him. He's such a jerk. You gotta know that by now."

"Yeah."

"Heather, your eyes are gorgeous. Don't let anyone tell you something different."

"God, Matt—Are you f'ing on the make? Jeez!"

She flicked her cigarette, trudged up a slight knoll, and headed out of the woods.

My face grew hot.

Damian, Scott, and Vernon cackled like crows—their derision aimed at both of us in equal measure, it seemed to me.

"Pathetic, man. How fuckin' desperate," Damian cracked.

Remembering a mangy cur—his only true friend, I said, "Better than the skanky mutt that follows *you* around."

Putdowns were never my strong suit.

A rare circumstance when she lightened up, laughter didn't come naturally to Heather. If it happened at all, a modest ripple trickled from the back of her throat and she'd stop, self-conscious, and try to suppress it—as if a morsel of food had been lodged there and she was forced to swallow in order to catch her breath. On that afternoon, she laughed out loud—although by then she'd almost reached the edge of the trail.

A few minutes passed, and I hiked out as well—leaving my friends to their gaudy, airbrushed and over-bosomed naked pictures. I didn't understand their obsession with fake boobs—but, like most adolescent boys, welcomed the opportunity to sneak a peek at female breasts of any form.

Most times Heather irritated me for sure, yet besides begrudging admiration for the manner in which she dealt with her circumstances, other types of sentiments were taking root. Although embarrassed, I was not ashamed of the kind words I'd spoken to her on that day.

In my early years, I'd found it easy to say what was on my mind. Fugitive emotions fled my brain—more often my heart—without fear of repercussion or ridicule. Of course, this trait was not always hailed by others. Once, during a kindergarten visit to Logan Airport, our class sat in a large double-propped military helicopter while the pilot explained his craft. Apparently, I'd quickly become bored and blurted out he "talked too much"—at least that's how my parents relayed the episode.

A grade school instructor told my mother—with some measure of astonishment—how I would compliment a classmate's drawing or the way a certain girl dressed. And—when distributing Valentine's cards to my fellow students—she'd note a caring comment I'd written about an assist a kid made when playing soccer or a passage another had read from an assignment. According to my mom, the teacher regarded it as unusual and an example of my "heightened observation skills."

I preferred to think the callow boy I was, someone I scarcely remembered, could have just been compassionate.

My dad liked to share—with all who would listen—a story about the time my sister and I traveled with them to New York City and stayed at the Americana Hotel. How he let us take the elevator downstairs to the lobby restaurant alone and—even though three years younger—handed me the money to pay for the meal because "Matt was the man." When we returned, Dad asked for the change; but I had no cash in my pockets.

"I gave her a big tip," I supposedly said.

"Why?"

"Because she had pretty cheeks, wavy hair, and smiled a lot."

Perhaps my teacher had adroitly assessed the situation after all, and these responses of mine were merely evidence of an ability to notice things. I came to believe the only reason it impressed my father was because—as the years progressed—it was a rare instance he could point to and prove to others I was "one of the guys" and it had nothing to do with my keen powers of observation.

As a kid, I'd hug a person if they did something

good—like hit a triple and knock in the winning run—or simply if I'd gotten the impression they needed one. This is what I've been told. No angel, I had a temper, and could dish out insults in anger with the best of them. But, early on, I believed in the importance of telling people how you felt—especially if those feelings were affirming. Over time, I deemed it necessary to ratchet down that behavior. In junior high, Michael Gray called me a "fag" and Bobby Boudreau accused me of acting "like a pansy"—all because I'd sometimes rather talk with the seventh- and eighth-grade girls than hang out with guys who hucked louies in massive globs and bragged about "getting it" from Jenny Pritchard behind the seawall.

When I got older, Dad often chided me by saying "For Christ's sake Matt, grow up" and other stuff if he determined my response to a particular event or person overly sensitive.

As a teenager, I frequently hesitated and then strained to form deliberate thoughts before each reply—an attempt to oblige my father by taking a stab at "growing up" no doubt. While some of it was because of what happened to Heather much later, the year we both turned fourteen.

A few months after the incident with Heather at the Indian Trail, my sister—who'd been away at college—came home with several dresses she had to alter for a theater production. I knocked to welcome her back and Francesca invited me into the bedroom. To my surprise, in front of the vanity sat Heather—dolled up in a flowing period gown that might've been from the 1940s. She'd always admired Franny.

My sister had brushed Heather's hair and tied it in a bun at the top of her head. She'd also applied makeup—almost certainly one of the first times Heather had ever worn it—along with a touch of eye shadow.

Heather's world-weary eyes stared at me—somehow projecting more wisdom than anyone else in that room, that house. Her blush painted cheeks and dimples seemed poised to combat any gloom she might face.

I lingered at the threshold, my fingers still on the door handle, mouth wide open.

Heather grabbed a brush and tossed it with the velocity of a shortstop attempting to make the second half of a double play. It missed my forehead by only a few inches, bounced off the wall, and fell to the floor.

"Matthew Dominico, if you dare tell a soul what you saw here, you'll pay for it. And for a long time. I swear."

— 12 —

Wearing the patchwork cloak she had on in Hartford the night we first met, Johanna briskly descended the Gate 17 ramp; a multicolored boa wrapped her neck. She spoke non-stop to a guy who sported a three-piece suit as well as the requisite boredom of someone who'd been re-turning from a business trip. Johanna spotted me, gave the man a bear hug, and trotted in my direction.

"I'm so glad to see you!" She dropped her car-ryon, grabbed my shoulders, and kissed me on each cheek—the gesture formal and playful at the same time. Pulling me closer, Johanna held me tight until I became a tad embarrassed by stares from people who passed by—most of whom smiled, though a few seemed content not to acknowledge her rainbow of energy.

"Did I tell you I'm so happy to see you?" she said.

I picked up her bag; she locked her arm in mine and we headed for the parking garage.

"I've never been to Boston. Hope we get a chance to visit the city. But I've got to be back in New Haven by Friday and with the interview tomorrow morning, that only leaves us a day or so free. Maybe. You never know. I'd love to check out the Gardner and the Museum of Fine Arts—I heard the Public Garden is gorgeous. Do you—"

"—How much caffeine did you have on the plane?"

During our last moments together, Johanna and I had just returned from a peacefully bucolic horseback ride and then a leisurely stroll to the gallery in Avon. So her current frenetic chatter startled me. I chalked it up to pre-interview jitters.

We breezed by a few kiosks and the tantalizing smells of roasting pretzels and fresh-brewed Dunkin Donuts coffee. The PA system broadcast arrival and departure announcements.

"I'm famished. You think we can grab something to eat?"

And at that moment I remembered she hadn't known I was *sans appartement*—as her friends in Provence might've said.

"That's alright," Johanna said when I told her. "Parents adore me!"

I hoped that was true.

81

Though already 9:30, a variety of sliced cold cuts, vinegar peppers, a cheese platter, and homemade bread from Previte's Bakery—still warm—covered the table.

Johanna embraced Mom, who handed her a glass of red wine. My mother encouraged her to sit—especially after Jo spoke about a delay in Bridgeport that caused her to miss supper—but Johanna walked to the den and studied my late dad's artwork, which hung on most of the downstairs walls—particularly in that room.

Portraits of friends and family members—as well as paintings of local seascapes, and islands in the South Pacific that began as wartime sketches while stationed there—were all part of the collection.

Johanna lingered at pieces featuring religious themes and a pastel of black and white children playing in the street—water gushed from an open inner-city fire hydrant while multifamily tenements loomed in the background. She touched—almost caressed—the works. Johanna had calmed considerably after our initial greeting at Logan. I didn't know if it was due to the effects of the ten-minute car ride, the cabernet, or my father's artwork. Whatever the reason, I welcomed it.

As years passed, I sometimes wondered if Dad—

the union tile guy—had been a frustrated artist. After leaving in his senior year before graduating, he joined the Navy and never made it to college once he returned home—dreams of an art major and career dashed by responsibilities to my aging grandparents and his own burgeoning household. So, he installed tile in kitchens and bathrooms by day, employing any flourishes he could when placing 4 x 4 or 6 x 6 pieces onto mastic adhesive—and on the rare occasions when a mosaic project for a chapel or restaurant presented itself. For the rest of his life, he took night classes at Boston University and the Museum of Fine Arts.

"They're marvelous," she whispered. "Not schooled at all."

Whatever that meant.

A burly man, with bulging arms bursting from an ever-present t-shirt, my father would've never been mistaken for a stereotypical painter—one who employed easel and beret while capturing a pastoral landscape—though his talent and avocation never disappeared. Many a night I'd discover him in our basement—crumbs of asbestos-ridden pipe insulation spitting onto his canvas from overhead and a smoky furnace belching by his side. He'd inevitably be drawing something from his South Pacific experiences or a pastel portrait of a niece, nephew, or close friend's kid while Nat King Cole sang "Nature Boy" over and over again from a Radio Shack cassette-tape player.

One day—during my junior year in high school—Dad grew impatient waiting for an apprentice who was supposed to help him lug several boxes of tile up the stairs of an East Boston triple-decker. Each box weighed over twenty-five pounds, and it wasn't unusual for my father to carry two or more at a time.

Returning from their break that afternoon, the apprentice and a plumber found Dad prone on the top landing, dead.

"Matthew tells me you're more than good, Johanna," my mother said before trying to hustle us towards the kitchen.

Jo paused at a family portrait resting on the console piano. "Who's this?" She pointed to the girl.

"My sister Francesca. That's Orlando, my brother, next to her."

We sat down. Johanna leapt up a few times to examine the caricatures hanging nearby: one, a humorous self-portrait of my father, the other a more serious rendering of my Uncle Sean, who dressed as a clown during Shiners' parades.

I glanced across the table. Ecstatic I'd returned home on the one hand—no matter how much I'd assured her it was only temporary—a part of my mother had been striving to get me married since I'd turned twenty, perhaps even earlier, on the other. And the look she gave Johanna that night resembled one a deep-sea fisherman might have while trying to haul in a prized catch.

Before Mom got an opportunity to ask her if she had anyone "special" in her life, I grabbed the wine bottle and took Johanna by the arm to check out the sleeping arrangements. At that moment, I wasn't certain I wanted to hear Johanna's answer to Ma's anticipated question.

She stopped at the piano and her fingers repeated a couple of light trills at the treble end.

"Who plays?"

"Matt used to. He was *wonderful*," Mom chimed in.

Johanna smiled when my face flushed.

After my father died, my mother lowered the heat for the two upstairs rooms; her bedroom was on the ground floor. I'd moved most of my stuff from the Chelsea apartment and divided it between her cellar and a second-floor room I once shared with my brother. Orlando's Bobby Orr and Johnny Unitas prints, Dad's painting of Clarabelle the Clown, and a placard of Olivia Hussey from the film *Romeo and Juliet* still hung on those walls. I'd gotten that movie poster when Arnie, from the five-and-dime, ripped it off his shop door and shoved it into my hands one day after becoming fed up with the way I froze—mesmerized by Hussey—every time I walked into the store, blocking any customer in my path.

While stacking stuffed cardboard boxes and plastic bins in that room, I could've sworn I'd detected a hint of my father's Old Spice—but knew it certainly wasn't possible after all those years had passed. I'd also discovered a ratty and faded loose-leaf book on my brother's and my battered desk. Between its covers were a half dozen 8 x 10 canvas panels with cartoon images of Superman, Underdog, and Mighty Mouse. One included Mister Peabody from the *Rocky and Bullwinkle* show, along with his sidekick Sherman—whose name my second-grade classmates had given me because of my oversized glasses.

My dad had drawn these when I was seven or eight. I had come down with a horrific flu—temperatures reaching 102 and higher—that triggered terrifying hallucinations. For several nights in a row, I strove to escape from teachers, neighbors, and faceless shadows who I insisted were hiding in my closet and under my bed.

While sitting with me for hours, hoping to calm me down, my father drew these superheroes.

I showed Johanna the guest room.

"Let me know if you need anything."

"Ordinarily, I'd feel sorry for you giving up your bed, Matt. And I do. But tonight I'm more than grateful. I'm bushed."

"Happy to do it."

And it was true. When I recalled the floors, couches, and chairs I'd slept on while traveling as a roadie or working for *Musician* and other mags, my mother's comfy sofa and cozy living room were, in contrast, first-class accommodations. I left Johanna alone to change clothes.

Jo joined me and sat in an easy chair. I poured us another glass of wine, then kneeled to browse through a bookcase; she leaned over to kiss me on the cheek. "I'll make it up to you," she said. After I'd sorted through a few books, I handed her an Anais Nin, an Austen, a Shepard title and one Orlando gave me—*Be Here Now*—that I couldn't get into.

Mom's slippers shuffled through the den and stopped before entering. "Good night, kids."

"Kids." I shook my head.

"She's sweet. Must be tough—on her own."

"Yeah. They were a rarity. Not a perfect match by any stretch. But still seemed in love after more than thirty years.

The way my father explained it, he spent most of his junior year in the high school cafeteria sketching pictures of my mother from afar, too intimidated to speak with her, until a mutual friend of theirs—unbeknownst to my dad—snatched a few and showed them to my mom. She struck up a conversation and asked him to join her and some friends for an evening of candlepin bowling on the boulevard. They hung with the group for quite a while and didn't officially date until he returned home from the war—Nervous about tomorrow?"

"What?"

"Your interview."

"Nah. They won't hire me."

"What do you mean?"

"The hallowed halls of Phillips Andover? Seriously?"

"Hey, you got invited, didn't you?"

"I suppose."

Johanna told me how she'd taught at U Madison in Wisconsin, and once she arrived in Connecticut she had teaching gigs at both Fairfield and Wesleyan. She spoke about the rituals that took place during the standard screening process for an artist or craftsperson.

"You have to lug all this stuff—35 millimeter slides, your assembled portfolio—and schlep them into a conference room. Sometimes there's a committee you're expected to meet with. Other times your work is placed on easels—a few samples are projected on a screen. You bare your soul and you're judged on your history and your talent by a professor who likes Warhol but may hate a more traditional artist like Millet. I used to research the school or person scheduled to interview me—maybe find an *ArtNews* article at the library. It won't matter really, because that person has changed her mind, or now hopes to shake things up by finding someone entirely different from their current curriculum and philosophy. And later, you're prompted to do something no artist ever wants to do—explain. *Tell the folks what's behind door number 3, Bob.* Share with people you've never met, in an unlit room, the deep-seated motivation that might've driven you to create this work of yours that's projected three or more times its intended size in front of you—as if you always know, anyway. So you try to be yourself—because that's all you can be, right? Then you think, this is Andover Academy; I can't be myself, or my true self. Can I? So—"

Johanna laughed. "I guess I *am* a little nervous."

"When do you have to be there?"

"The interview is ten to noon. After that, I'm hoping we'll see a lot of the exhibits featured at the Addison."

Jo looked at the book covers I'd given her, picked the Austen and rose from her chair.

"Thank you again." She kissed my cheek and headed for the bedroom.

$$-\ 13\ -$$

On the ride north to Andover, Johanna reached out, grabbed my right hand, and wouldn't let go until we drove through the school's main gates.

With her appointment scheduled for ten, I told Johanna I'd stroll through the grounds and meet her at the gallery around noontime. I sat for a few moments in the Cochran Chapel—a building with elaborate archways, vaulted ceilings, and tall palladium windows. Someone played a solemn, single-note-sounding hymn on the organ; two cherub-like statues stared from above. Afterwards, I walked across the quad's manicured lawns and passed a phallic-looking sculpture before stopping to lean against a vast Armillary Sphere—a sort of sundial—cast in Paris by Paul Manship. The piece included a man and woman propping up a child.

Students ambled past, engaged in conversation,

textbooks in hand—images that could have been tak-en from the academy's recruitment catalogue. A boy leaned against a tree and read; I shook my head and wondered what my experiences would have been had I escaped the grasp of family and city and lived away on a high school campus. Would I have recog-nized it as a gift, or just one more path to isolation? When Johanna had poked fun of her artistic phases, it got me thinking about what I could only describe as my lost years. Semesters and summers that zoomed by in a cloud of tangled thoughts, leaving few tangible memories to bookmark.

Johanna joined me on the Addison steps.

"It went relatively well. But, I'm answered out." She sighed. "I'll fill you in later. Promise."

This time, I'd done a little homework at the Chel-sea Library for the occasion and learned what I could about several of the artists who would be represent-ed that afternoon. Although the gallery's four front columns were striking, its exterior proved under-whelming. Every section where you would expect a window was filled in by red bricks. Inside, works by Cassatt, Copley, Sargent, Prendergast, Whistler, and Homer were displayed in both conventional and con-temporary exhibition rooms.

Johanna wandered off, and I looked at some of

Hopper's early oil paintings—including *Freight Cars Gloucester* and *Railroad Train*. They spoke to my long-standing fascination with trains; the working- and lower-working-class geography and theme also drew me in. It had been rumored Hopper hadn't sold his first painting until he was forty years old; this gave me hope. I stood before Winslow Homer's *Kissing the Moon* and *Eight Bells*—the sea's fury and power menacing in both. Not familiar with his wood engravings, I discovered *A Winter Morning Shoveling Out* and similar stuff until Johanna turned up and led me to a large canvas of Georgia O'Keeffe's.

Wave Night—with its contours and use of pinkish purples and deep blues—reminded me of a couple of pieces from Johanna's *Womanscape* series. Minimalist, almost abstract—but not entirely so—it differed from any O'Keeffe image I'd viewed before in my limited experience. My research and visit to Jo's studio did not make me an art expert by any means; but I hoped the new language I was endeavoring to learn would provide me with a modicum of insight as well as an additional method of communicating with Johanna.

O'Keeffe's representation of a York Beach, Maine shoreline seemed to comfort her. Though previously introduced to this painting, Jo was captivated, as if for the first time. She nudged me across the hall to

Light Is Gold—a mixed piece of glass, lacquer, gold leaf—"and casein," Johanna informed me. Whatever that was. The artist, Irene Rice Pereira, was born in Chelsea—a bit of info I had *not* gleaned from my local library.

We moved on to images of Francesca Woodman posed in abandoned Victorian-era buildings. One photograph showed her partially swallowed by a brick fireplace; while in another she lay half-buried by sturdy, overturned dining room tables. Finally, we segued to Mary Cassatt's *Mother and Child in Boat*. Up to that point, I'd naively considered Cassatt traditional until Johanna related the story behind the artist's lost mural—a massive 58 x 12 foot panel. It had been commissioned as part of The Women's Building featured in the 1893 World Columbian Exhibition and Fair. Divided into three separate sections, *Young Women Plucking the Fruits of Knowledge or Science* comprised one component.

"Can you imagine how scandalous that must have been at the time?" she asked me.

The subject: women engaged in the arts as well as the pursuit of education, and Cassatt's adoption of bright colors, caused quite a stir—with some even speculating it had been maliciously destroyed after the Exhibition closed.

Years before—after enrolling in an Impression-ism course at the Gardner Museum—it occurred to me Cassatt had shown a great deal of courage when she left the country and made her way amid those French male painters, but I had no inkling of the rev-olutionary feminist piece Jo spoke about that day. I'd never look at Cassatt's work in the same manner.

Less than ten percent of the works at the Addison were by women—a higher number than in many other galleries or museums—yet Johanna not only located most of these, she could tell me a little about each.

Jo strayed again, and I studied John Koch's *The Toast*. A man offered his glass in celebration; but the woman he directed those efforts to gazed off into the distance.

The ride to Revere was quiet—I'd been more than overwhelmed by the art, and Johanna appeared to be undergoing a decompression of sorts. I slipped into cajoling mode, hoping to coax Jo from her doldrums, only to receive monosyllabic responses from her in return.

Undeterred, I plodded on, "You think—"

Then—much to my surprise and relief—I stopped, realizing Johanna would be better served if

I repressed these long-held desires of mine to retain control and dispel silence. It was time for me to find other methods of providing solace.

I switched on the radio and cycled through channels—in an ardent quest for Muzak and not something that might challenge us.

Hearing subdued sobs, I dropped my hand from the steering wheel and caressed Johanna's shoulders.

"Stunning. Simply magnificent," she said, still looking forward, unaware of my touch.

I wasn't sure if these were tears of sadness—or exaltation after having been in the presence of such genius and splendor.

"How will I ever get there?" she whispered before turning to face me.

— 14 —

Antipasto, tiny meatballs, tossed salad, a bowl of chicken legs, and three types of pasta spread across the kitchen counter; it made me wonder who else Mom had invited to this feast.

Polite but subdued, Johanna helped clear the table and load the dishwasher after she "couldn't swallow another bite." She rinsed a couple of large pans in the sink, and my mother hustled her away. Before leaving the room, Johanna poured a glass of wine, kissed her, and said, "I'm drained and gonna crash. You don't mind?"

"Course not."

I joined Mom and tidied up, but couldn't remember what cabinet to place the glasses in and where the oversized bowls were supposed to go. Then I knocked on Johanna's door. Images of daisies, cows, and cheese wedges dotted her robe.

"Cool threads."

"Don't ask." She smiled. "A gift from my niece."

"You OK?"

"Just tired."

"Those interviews can take a lot out of you."

"I guess. Between that and the traveling. It's been a whirlwind twenty-four hours."

"I've got nothing fancy or stressful planned for tomorrow."

"That'll be different—a nice change."

"Pleasant dreams," I said.

I grabbed the Shepard book, sat on the couch, put on a Jackson Browne cassette and fell asleep—not yet nine, my clothes were still on.

On the way to Revere Beach, I remembered what Johanna had shared about Riverside Cemetery in Appleton; so I swung by Rumney Marsh Burial Ground. Markers from as far back as the late seventeenth century stood there. Johanna paused at tombstones for a two-month-old and a five-and-a-half-year-old, a young mother who died in childbirth, a Civil War Congressional Medal of Honor winner, and a teenaged-boy who drowned. A few chickadees followed us—flitting from stone to stone. I thought of a family cross-country camping trip that included a stop at a Deadwood, South Dakota cemetery, which housed dozens of graves marking the lives of women in their teens and early twenties.

I told Johanna the whole purpose of the Revere site was to locate land north of Boston where small-pox victims could be buried and not risk exposing the people who lived within the confines of the state capital. Several other poor souls ended up there as well.

"How lonely it must have been," Johanna said.

"What do you mean?"

"Bad enough folks didn't want to be close to you during the rages of an epidemic—while you were alive and breathing—they found it necessary to iso-late you even after you died . . . I hung out at Kitty Blood's gravestone because—though two centuries had already gone by—they still wouldn't let her rest in peace. Sometimes I simply hoped to comfort her." She shook her head. "Ridiculous, of course."

I didn't know what to say.

Johanna strolled to a commemorative tablet mounted in homage to slaves, who'd been interred in unmarked graves near the ivy-covered outer walls. She bowed. After a few minutes, Jo placed a finger to her lips and dabbed the top of the plaque; then she turned around, grasped my arm, and we walked to the car.

A scant fifteen-minute subway ride from downtown Boston stood Revere Beach—three miles of crescent-shaped coast and safe undertow-free swimming.

I held Johanna's hand and strolled along what remained of the boardwalk. We passed the skeletal studs and wooden strapping of the Cyclone—a rickety roller coaster that once rose over a hundred feet and whose track ran for more than half a mile. Remnants of the Tilt-A-Whirl and Himalaya rides—bending and moaning in a slight breeze—looked and sounded like newsreel footage after a tornado had blown through the area. This posed in sharp contrast to the soundtrack of its glory days: peals of laughter, pulsing calliope chords, and nonstop rhythm surging from Motown tunes that blared from ubiquitous and staticky speakers. Smells of garlic-teemed tomato sauce, fried clams, and onion rings from the last remaining food joints—Bianchi's, Bill Ash's, Kelly's—wrestled defiantly with salt sea air in testimony to that legacy. On our one and only "date," I bought 25-cent slices of pizza on this boulevard for Sheila Giannino and me to eat during a return walk to her house. In better years, the movies *Love Story*, *The Friends of Eddie Coyle*, and *Loose Change* had scenes filmed here;

Barbra Streisand and Frank Sinatra made early appearances at the Frolic and Surf clubs.

Johanna and I headed for the shoreline, removed our shoes and socks at the water's edge; waves lapped our feet. The Nahant peninsula jutted out on the horizon; a few moored boats bobbed in the distance; an older man tugged on the string of his kite— a boxed affair in red, white, and blue.

After walking for a while, we came upon a young boy and girl. A half-buried pail and shovel rested next to them; they were digging with their hands.

I bent over. "Searching for Gold?"

"Clams, silly."

"Can I help?"

Without waiting for an answer, I peered into the shallows and searched for the telltale sign: oxygen bubbles breaking the sand's surface. With both hands, I scraped a hole until I touched the tip of a quahog shell. I dug furiously and deep before scooping my prize—together with dripping clumps of mud.

The kids' laughs were infectious; Johanna joined me—now on both knees as well.

"'Show me how, mister," said the girl, gazing at my muck-covered hands.

"Yeah. Show me, *mister*," Johanna piped in before

hugging me from behind and kissing the top of my head.

I pointed out a few more air holes. Before long, they found another large clam, and Johanna and I helped them grab it.

We stood, dusted ourselves off, and continued to stroll.

"You must have swum here every chance you got as a kid," she said.

Gentle swells of sparkling water broke softly. Seagulls hovered above the clam-digging pair—a football field or more away by then.

I squinted at the peninsula across the bay; a light salt spray spritzed my face, and I mulled the best way of responding. This didn't seem the right moment to explain why I'd stopped swimming.

"Not swam as much as hung out, I guess."

"I've never learned to swim. Can do a pretty mean dog paddle, though."

I told Johanna about my swimming lessons— which took place two miles south of where we were standing—near the Winthrop town border, on a somewhat private stretch of sand called Short Beach. I'd been avoiding it; but our parents insisted we learn. So, late in August, a few weeks before school began, I trekked the mile from my house alone to meet a Red Cross trainer at the first ramp. Four other kids around my age and I attempted to master the breast and butterfly strokes as well as how to float in the three-to-four-foot swells driven into shore by deadly strong west winds. In hindsight, though I swallowed more than my allotted share of saltwater, it was a practical teaching method. Those treacherous conditions gave me the only motivation I needed. The attractive auburn-haired instructor, who couldn't have been more than twenty, was kind and patient—obviously bored—and no doubt dying to return to college. During those waning days of summer the beach was vacant, except for a few hopeful elderly couples in lawn chairs who prayed for sunlight to poke through overcast skies, despite the onslaught of waves that had turned more white-capped than blue and other harbingers of autumn's swift approach.

We walked towards a lengthy sandbar that once served as the foundation for Holt's Pier and—even earlier than that—had made up a portion of the sea-bed on which the Old Pier Dancing Pavilion had been constructed.

Jo spoke of a trip to Florida she'd taken years before. The day had been a delight until her niece stepped on several barnacles. "I picked her up. Feet bleeding. Rushed her to my brother's car and the hospital. Stacy's only concern was that we left her doll—without friends—leaning against a boulder near the shore."

Johanna combed wind-blown hair from my face with her hand. "I'm sorry. Not sure why I brought that up. It was the last time I've been on the coast—and we'd been having such a fine adventure til then."

"Had to be scary."

She motioned to an abandoned ride across the street. "How did this happen?"

"What?"

"The waterfront. How'd it get this way?"

I discussed the brief four- or five-month season when companies were required to earn their total annual profit and pay twelve months' worth of taxes. Then, I referenced the underworld element. If they hadn't owned a major percentage of the amusements and associated businesses themselves, they often were in control of the real estate on which those firms sat. And, by the end of the sixties, organized crime—in addition to second-generation members of long-standing law-abiding family owners—soon discovered the benefits of much more dependable revenue streams than amusement rides, concessions, and nightclubs. Not to mention by the early '70s, "destination" vacations had become the vogue. Run-down honky-tonks, rusty Ferris wheels, and shooting galleries were few folks' idea of a satisfactory destination, with the possible exception of lower-working-class residents from nearby inner cities—only a Blue Line subway ride away—bikers from the Hell's Angels and Devil's Disciples, and Revere's own.

The shore now empty—apart from squawking gulls and the kite flyer—we reached the sandbar and searched for sea glass. Dock pilings jutted from the ocean in crisscross fashion. An accidental weir, these were the only vestiges of Holt's Pier and the old Dancing Pavilion. Their rotting green and brown seaweed-covered wood formed ragged patterns like crucifixes in a graveyard.

Johanna sat on a huge bolder and looked at the horizon. With a piece of driftwood, she scraped lines and other shapes in the sand, then pulled a sketch pad from her pocketbook.

The setting sun cast ominous shadows on the water's surface, like those distorted images I used to make while mugging in front of mirrors at Hurley's Funhouse—which once stood forty yards away. Angry waves slapped pilings. A considerably pungent sea spray that had long before claimed squatter's rights to this area of the beach grew stronger. Some blamed raw sewage that occasionally spilled from the neighboring Deer Island treatment plant. Others alleged different—more sinister—reasons.

A part of me wanted to snatch the pad from Johanna's hands as she had done to me during our picnic in Avon, yet I didn't dare.

"Tell me about this section. I sense an intensity—a presence—that's still here."

Because of the new-age-mystic vibe she'd been giving off—and since she appeared to detect something otherworldly—I needed to avoid a vacuous silence. So, I told Johanna about the once magnificent ballroom, the lights that dotted its wharf, the couples dancing, and the music—all of which I'd only seen in old faded photographs and postcards or heard of from stories shared by my grandparents, parents, and their friends. Then, I described Holt's Pier—the less ostentatious structure built after fires and storms destroyed the great pavilion.

"We rented dories from Holt—I caught my first flounder there."

Seagulls squealed, landed, and fought to outrace the rushing torrent—their stick legs and webbed feet stopped and started haphazardly—like the flickering frames of an eight millimeter black-and-white silent home movie.

I stared at a strip of breakwater that bordered

what was once the dock's south side.

"A kid drowned here," I said softly.

Waves crashed and forced me a few steps backwards.

Johanna didn't move.

I shivered before fumbling to fasten the buttons of my shirt.

Jo put the pencil tip to her mouth, closed her eyes, and tilted her head. "Oh." She made an abbreviated sign of the cross.

I wasn't sure why I'd raised the subject. It could've been because Johanna had been facing elsewhere and sketching—fully engaged in an activity she loved—and no one was around. Perhaps it was because of a momentary sense of security—although the wrath from the incoming tide had brought forth splashing waves with an ever-increasing fury, causing the seagulls to abandon their competition and take off. Still, amid that turmoil, being with Johanna allowed a sort of calm to sneak its way inside me—a sensation I hadn't experienced in some time, and certainly not whenever I stood near the shore.

I pondered sharing the whole story of that drowning, but had no interest in dampening the mood of what had been an exceedingly pleasant day.

I hunted for a few thin stones to skip upon the water. Having no luck with my search, I grabbed a handful of round, chestnut-colored pebbles, scattered them into the air, and watched as they broke the ocean's plane.

The quarter-mile stretch of breakwater running perpendicular to us was flat on top and remarkably deceptive; it enabled you to walk its entire length, then sit and contemplate the surrounding water. If you weren't careful and the tide rolled back in, an unforgiving and raging surf would envelop you on all sides. Before too long, you might discover yourself isolated and alone in the middle of it.

I sent another batch of sea-washed stones to the murky bottom, then sauntered towards Johanna, and kissed her forehead. She flipped over the sketch she'd been working on: full of shadows and light, it reminded me of Monet's haystacks.

Mom kissed, then hugged Johanna. "Hope to see you again . . . soon. *Soon*. Got that?" Jo smiled.

On the ride to the airport, I stopped at Belle Isle Marsh—nestled on the Revere/East Boston line. I drove to the entrance of the old Suffolk Downs Drive-In—which had once covered most of this tract of land—and pulled up over curb and sidewalk before skirting past Jersey barriers meant to block the road leading inside. Johanna had no idea where we were bound; the massive neon marquee, replete with its animated arrow and movie listings, had been demolished years before.

"What are you doing? We're gonna be late. If this is a shortcut, I'm not sure I like it."

"Plenty of time."

I had seen *Mary Poppins* and other films there as a kid. But, between the roar of low-flying planes landing and taking off from nearby Logan—which made critical sections of dialogue inaudible—and the squadrons of ravenous mosquitoes that launched from surrounding wetlands and swarmed patrons on their way to the snack bar, this ill-advised location for an open-air theater, as they used to call them, was abandoned. The Parks and Recreation Department then allowed native flora and fauna to reclaim its territory and turned the acreage into a state-protected conservation reserve.

"Matthew?"

"Shssh . . . Listen and . . . watch."

The final glimpses of a setting sun faded in the west. Even though several steel pillars that once held speakers still surrounded us and the weed-infiltrated, crumbling cement blocks of the movie screen's foundation were visible, birds and wildlife of every variety had repopulated land and marsh.

We gazed southeast and watched a snowy egret take flight from shallow water and reeds. Sandpipers and sparrows dotted the landscape; an owl called out.

The Battle of Chelsea Creek, the first naval engagement of the Revolutionary War, had its origins here after a few starving British soldiers attempted to steal cows from a neighboring farm. For only a moment, I considered sharing that saga with Johanna. But I'd driven to this oasis to speak of the future—not to recount some history lesson from the Louis Pasteur Elementary School.

A few other birds took off and landed in the distance; saltgrass danced in a mild wind. Tenderly, I caught hold of Johanna's arms before leaning in to kiss her on the lips.

"Uhmm. That was nice," she said.

When I moved closer to kiss her a second time, she gently pushed me away.

"I can't." She pointed to her wristwatch.

"Johanna, I'm confused. What's the deal?"

"We've had a great couple of days. Must we get into this now?"

"When exactly are we *supposed* to get into *this*?"

She exhaled. "It's complicated."

"Jesus!" I shouted louder than I'd intended and slid against the driver's side door. Mom's car was only a Chevy Nova sedan; yet two people couldn't have been further apart.

"Please," she said in half whisper. "I care for you. We've become good friends."

"Friends?!"

"Yes. *Friends*." Barely audible, Johanna had emphasized—lingered on—her last word with a kind of

111

reverence. "Is that such a bad thing?"

"I want more," I insisted, with an immature petulance I'd be ashamed of later.

I guess I should have said *need* more.

And then, embarrassed—mortified—I started the car, turned it around, and headed for the airport.

Thank God our drive to Logan was less than five minutes; the silence grew frightening. Johanna reached out and placed her hand over mine. When I didn't move my own from the steering wheel, she pulled hers from me, then fumbled in her purse for the plane ticket.

We arrived a half hour before takeoff. For a few seconds or so I thought about dropping Jo off, giving her a buss on the cheek and then handing over the carryon before leaving her in front of Eastern's sliding glass doors. But I realized I'd been acting like a jerk, so I parked and hustled with Johanna to Gate 22.

The screams of a reluctant toddler being hauled in tow by a parent nearly drowned out overhead announcements.

We approached the attendant at the counter and I handed Johanna the suitcase.

"I can't leave it—us—this way." She kissed me.

"We're fine." I forced a smile.

Johanna walked a few feet in the ramp's direction, turned, and ran towards me. She dropped her bag and gave me a bear hug.

"I do too," she whispered in my ear.

"What?"

"Want more."

Then, teary-eyed, she rushed up the ramp and out of sight.

East 7th
& Newbury Streets

— 16 —

Over the next few months came an exchange of letters and telephone calls. During that period, Johanna took up a former college classmate's offer to move from Connecticut to New York City and into an East Village apartment with this friend and another woman.

I accepted one of Johanna's countless invitations to visit. The Metroliner made sense, I reasoned. More room, better views, I'd arrive at Penn Station—much closer to the heart of the things—and this option was less expensive than a round trip flight and cab. All these arguments were convincing enough, but my overriding fear of flying drove me to choose this route.

The last time I'd ridden on a train was as a kid with my sister—destination also the Big Apple and the setting of my father's "tip" anecdote. Francesca and I created a contest to find out how many cars we could pass through on the way to the dining carriage before we'd lose our balance and get jostled against walls and seats. How easy it was to regain our footing in those days. Years before Johanna ever spoke to me about the locomotives that rolled past the Fox River in Appleton, I understood the yearning a simple clang of a crossing gate, or the wistful sound of a distant whistle could stir. Although until then, the only trains I'd been familiar with were those from the crowded Blue Line subway that screeched and clacked and woke me up with a vengeance during their initial 5:45 a.m. run of the morning—a reminder a new school day approached.

I glanced at a Roman-numeraled clock hanging from the ceiling of South Station and out towards the half dozen empty rows of track.

At sixteen in Nevada, during a family camping vacation, I'd walked along rails—except those lay baking in a Southwestern sun. A zebra-tailed lizard froze at first, then scurried when I bent to pick up an abandoned license plate riddled with bullet holes. I ventured over a rust-permeated trestle. Its splintered ties and vine-choked supports all but assuring that soon some passing locomotive would end up crashing into the dried bed of a used-to-be creek below.

When I stopped at a single-pump gas station/general store on the dirt road that had criss-crossed the tracks several times, a guy rode in on an Indian motorcycle, slipped coins into the soda machine, and handed me a bottle of Coke before getting one for himself.

"Gotta shake sand off before heading out again," he said and invited me to shoot a game of pool.

In his mid-twenties, he didn't speak to me as the green kid I was, but asked about the books I was reading. We touched on Richard Brautigan—who I believed fantastic at the time—and Steinbeck, then played maybe three games. Though I hardly got an opportunity to use my cue stick—the guy was that good.

Afterwards, he bought me a burger and told me of his plans to reach North Carolina, and a girl he'd left behind. The *d* and two *e*'s from an Old Milwaukee neon sign flickered. "Spirit in the Sky" blared from a jukebox in the corner; sawdust covered the ravaged wooden floor.

Before leaving, he revved the bike's throttle repeatedly, leaned in my direction and said, "Thanks for the chat. Just be yourself." He sped off in a cloud of gritty dust and I stared until the peace symbol sewn onto the back of his denim jacket disappeared from view.

I didn't have a clue who "myself" was; yet this stranger recognized a someone.

Years later, when I watched the movie *Paris, Texas*, I thought of Reno. In the opening scenes, the main character walks alone out of the desert in search of family, a woman, a past. I'm not sure why, but I'd needed to watch that film again and again, which I managed to until Becky—my girlfriend at the time—tossed the VHS tape into the trash with disgust.

An incoming fog draped the few arriving trains. From the mist, a young soldier in uniform bounded down a couple of stairs, dropped his bag, and gave a long and tight hug to the woman who greeted him. Two kids shouted "Daddy" and ran towards a man with outstretched arms. Speakers announced departures and echoed. I made my way through the haze, skirted by a teenager on skateboard, then joined the burgeoning crowd shuffling to track 9 and New York.

— 17 —

With a minute to spare, I got to the Bleecker Street Cinema in time for Johanna to kiss me, grab my hand, and hustle us inside for Marjorie Keller's *Daughters of Chaos*—the scheduled feature of a women's film festival the theater was hosting.

Several camera angles shown that night—shot extremely low and not quite waist high—brought to mind stories I'd read of *Citizen Kane.* In that picture, Orson Welles dug a trench in the floor in order to capture a perspective that had rarely, if ever, been seen before.

By filming with handheld cameras through windows and chain-link fences, Keller created her own series of fractured images and mosaic visions.

The movie's primary subject: marriage, forced me to think of rituals, and the role we all play in perpetuating them. Sitting in the dark, I reflected on my

121

situation—what I wanted versus what Johanna *needed.* It was a confusing era for anyone hoping to find a room of one's own.

When the film ended, Johanna, three women she'd just met, and I walked along Bleecker to the Surf Maid pub—a block away. In the corner, a duo, one woman at the piano, another on an upright bass, launched into "Stardust"—a version less ballad-driven and more rollicking than what I'd been accustomed to hearing.

Only 8 p.m. or so—still early for the Village—it pleased Johanna that the place was barely three-quarters full. I dawdled for a few minutes, wondering if I should ask the women what they'd like to drink. Would that gesture be perceived as an insult, as if a woman wasn't capable of—or couldn't afford—ordering a Black Russian for herself and then hauling it to the table alone?

An elaborate Budweiser sign—replete with galloping Clydesdales and small hunting dogs—spun and shimmered above our heads.

I hoped not to embarrass Johanna, but finally asked, "What can I get for you girls?"

Girls. I winced.

Thankfully, my use of the term didn't cause a stir—perhaps because they had tossed "girlfriend" around during their initial responses to *Chaos.*

Johanna snagged a table in the club's outside patio section. Though the winter had been mild up to that point—and heaters hung from awnings with clear plastic siding in place—it surprised me they'd kept this part of the restaurant open.

I set down a couple of wines, a beer, a spring water, and a glass of amoretto before edging my chair closer to the sidewalk. Then I watched these new friends converse—after having met only a half hour before. In chatting about the movie, they referenced authors that included Sand and Lessing; and spoke of Morisot, Brooks, and others. I told myself I shouldn't have been stunned by the breadth of knowledge they possessed—this was a Keller film and not *Indiana Jones* or *Gremlins.*

"It reminded me of Colette," Donna said. "I'm not certain why. It could've been Keller's attempts to evoke the senses."

Johanna nodded. "Which is a challenge to portray on screen—still, I know what you mean. Maybe because of Colette's view of traditional *'roles*?'" Johanna employed air quotes. "Or because they also criticized her stuff for lack of plot?"

Donna patted her on the shoulder; just a sample of the many subtle gestures—taps on a hand, a touch

123

on the forearm—the women made during their conversation. I couldn't imagine four guys, after so recently being introduced, engaging in this type of dialogue—at least the men I'd known.

I observed them connect in celebration, bearing
witness to an extraordinary event. My sense of wonder could've been because of the alcohol, the cumula-
tive exhaustion of an exceedingly long day or, more
likely, the fact men and women communicated on
entirely different levels. Johanna had already nick-
named me "the skeptic," and until that moment, I
wouldn't have believed in the possibility of this kind
of warm exchange among strangers.

Seeing how quickly they'd taken to Johanna filled
me with pride.

Its barbeque specialties put the Surf Maid on the
map and they smelled wonderful—so much so the
predominantly vegetarian Johanna sampled chicken
and ribs from my plate.

After coming back with an order of drinks, Alison asked my opinion.

I laughed. "An awful lot of red."

Courtney tugged at the cuff of her blazer for a
second. "That color can signify love—as when Keller
framed shots of the rose—and life itself. The young

girl's red bathing suit was no accident. It represents hemorrhaging—a loss of innocence and childhood. Astonishing what we've garnered from a movie that didn't last thirty minutes."

"That's a revelation about the filmmaker—as well as us," Alison said.

Johanna leaned forward. "Though you've got to be receptive for it to happen."

"The humor caught me off guard," I said. "It *is* a prerequisite for artists, I suppose."

Jo smiled. "I wish they'd offered that class in school. I would've been willing to learn."

The others agreed.

Another hour passed in quick fashion. During which I learned: Alison taught at a junior college while Donna, a performance artist, worked at a nearby gallery and was watching the son of her brother who'd been transferred to a different Air Force base, and Courtney, a secretary at E.F. Hutton, tended to her mother, who had taken ill.

Despite my prior concerns of giving offense, something deep within me, something family-driven, Revere-bred—both possibly—convinced me to pick up the tab. To my surprise, little pushback surfaced, instead a smattering of gracious "Thank yous."

They exchanged hugs and telephone numbers. I

took Johanna by the arm and headed for her place. Now after 2 a.m., I still lugged the gym bag I'd packed for the trip.

My legs grew heavier as we trudged up each successive cement stair to Johanna's sixth-floor apartment. She unlocked the door and nudged it forward; then put a finger to her lips and whispered, "They're probably asleep."

Jo directed me to a small alcove off the living room, where someone had previously unfolded a sofa bed. She disappeared before returning with sheets and blankets, which she placed on its mattress. Pointing to a half bath, she kissed me on the cheek. "We'll catch up tomorrow. Promise."

One of Johanna's roommates woke first and greeted me as I shuffled from the bed, sleep in my eyes.

"Morning. I'm Louise." She dropped a *Village Voice* on an easy chair next to hers and headed for the kitchen.

When I returned from the bathroom, Louise had set an *E.T.* mug on an end table, along with a carton of cream and packets of sugar.

"Yours." She nodded in the cup's direction. "You

have a good time last night?"

"Interesting. Not my usual flick."

"Wasn't quite *Footloose?*" She snickered. "Jo loves to drag folks to those kinds of events. I've almost run out of excuses."

"Didn't think it was *that* bad."

I longed to tell Louise I hadn't felt compelled in the least. But wasn't sure I'd be capable of articulating what I'd experienced the previous evening and — even if able—I couldn't imagine she'd understand.

"Johanna wanted me to go with you guys. I'm not the crusader she is."

Louise stated this in a straightforward manner; her observation didn't appear to be criticism.

Jo entered the room carrying a watering can; she kissed my forehead and approached the bay windows. I left to get her a cup of coffee.

"How was your night?" Johanna said when I came back.

I answered her question before realizing she'd been propping a leaf, speaking to the plants, and not me.

As part of her treats, Johanna planned a stop at a bookstore and tickets to the Janis Ian show at the Bottom Line.

We walked eight blocks to the Strand.

"You were a trouper last night." She held the door open for me.

Johanna grabbed a New York baseball cap from a merchandise display in the Sports section, struggled to place it on me, and teased, "I'll make you a Yankees fan yet."

I ducked and eluded her maneuvers a few times. She ultimately landed it sideways on top of my head before I ripped it off and flung it onto a shelf.

"Sorry. What's wrong?"

"Nothing."

I kissed Johanna, took her hand, and skirted past Biography towards Entertainment.

We strode by large cases stocked with oversized coffee-table books featuring Broadway shows and musicals. I considered calling my sister, who worked in Manhattan as an artistic director for an opera company. But the last occasion we'd been together could best be described as a strained family gathering, so I hesitated. It amazed me how each of us contained ourselves and suppressed any grievances we thought—we knew—we could stake claim to. The only evident eruptions were the sporadic and petty snipe fests that rolled in like unexpected thunder booms escorting a surprise spring shower. They departed just as swiftly—the long-term damage deposited in their wakes not readily perceptible.

Before Johanna and I left the Strand, she bought a hardcover copy of *Candide,* the *All Things Must Pass* album for me, and an Al Green cassette tape for her.

It didn't take more than the Bottom Line show's starting time—11 p.m.—to prove to me I wasn't in Kansas any longer. I couldn't remember a Boston performance of any sort—other than perhaps the headline act in a Combat Zone strip joint—beginning that late.

Cramped but intimate, the club accommodated four hundred people and the stage stood only three feet above ground. I knew Ian's popular songs, including "Society's Child," and "At Seventeen." Yet several tunes unfamiliar to me were what hit home— "Stars" and "Fly Too High" especially. Ian sang about the perils of performing, isolation, and rejection. The emotions she evoked ranged from profound loss and grief to glee. In "I Would Like to Dance," she glided good-naturedly across the floor to an accompanying samba beat.

The tempo slowed during "In The Winter" when Ian captured the heartbreak of confronting an old lover and his new wife. Percussive piano chords mixed hauntingly with bass notes. A staccato of drum slaps piled on additional blows. *I'm not afraid,* Ian vowed repeatedly; a few extra blankets in the winter will suffice she strove to convince herself.

When the singer started "Jesse," a romantic ballad of longing and sorrow, Johanna leaned forward in rapt attention, despite the asshole in the crowd who shrieked and cat-whistled after recognizing the song's introductory bars.

I would come to appreciate Jo's behavior during these types of performances. While most of us might've fallen back against our chairs—willing to be convinced but passively receiving—Johanna edged to the front of her seat, intent on capturing every nuance, a participant as well as an observer.

As a reporter, I'd learned to acknowledge such basic essentials as lighting, a show's pace, song sequence, phrasing—whether the band members were in sync. Jo recognized other aspects of the presentation. Johanna's face registered whenever Ian cracked a wry smile, or offered a slight roll of her eyes—or when some musical component surprised her—like a half note inserted into a live rendition of a tune where it hadn't been included in the original recording. More often than not, this kind of stuff passed over other folks' heads.

That night, none of those technical or staging elements mattered. I gazed at Johanna's profile—the mix of soft blue and emerald spotlights highlighting the supple contours of her neck—content to let it be.

— 18 —

Johanna's roommates had already gone to bed, and I'd yet to meet Rachel.

Two tall plants framed one of the three bay windows that overlooked Tompkins Square Park. Earlier that day, I'd asked Jo why she didn't just keep perennials in her flower pots and planters or—even better—replace them with plastic lifelike versions instead of the mix of annuals that forced her to repot every season.

"Gardening's got nothing to do with reason," she'd said.

Gauzy halos dotted lampposts and hovered over Christmas-light strings hanging from trees below. The bright green Chrysler Building crown beckoned in the background. A few cabs stopped; specks of people hopped out and headed for the park while others crossed the street. Snow flurries tumbled by. I felt detached from the world—and still a part of it.

Johanna walked up beside me, clasped her hand in mine—then twined our fingers together.

"Someday I want to make movies," I said.

Johanna grasped me tighter.

I think my blurting that out had less to do with films and more with my need to capture and frame the joy I'd been experiencing. If it were possible to record these feelings, I guessed it might've proven them legitimate. It wasn't often I'd been able to accept the solemn intimacy of a shared silence.

Then dread overtook me. I imagined it might be akin to what Johanna's experience had been in France. Would I ever be aware of this type of bliss again? Could it be real?

We watched a couple walking a dog until they vanished in twirls of white flakes.

"Gotta crash," Johanna said.

When we turned around, Jo's hand clung to mine. I attempted to separate and move towards the alcove with sofa bed; she held on, gently guiding me into her bedroom.

Remembering that first meeting with Johanna and the sparkling glitter in her hair, I expected to find iridescent stars fixed to her ceiling—the kind you might've seen in a kid's room. But a delicate pale blue washed the space and a lit table lamp shone from the corner. The low light illuminated sketches and posters on her walls—as well as looming silhouettes from an Anwar Sadat bobblehead and a plaster of Paris bust of Louis Armstrong that sat on a bureau. Beneath one sketch, which depicted a sad-looking-woman and appeared to be Johanna's handiwork, someone had scrawled the phrase: *The missing jack & ace.* A large poster titled "You Can't Swim in the Same River Twice" hung above her headboard; it featured a waterfall and rapids.

Johanna stripped.

I unbuckled my belt and slid my jeans down.

She tenderly removed my t-shirt and helped tug my briefs off before turning to climb on the bed.

After I leaned in for a kiss, my tongue soon probing, Johanna nudged me aside.

"Where's the fire?" she said.

Memories of our time in Avon, Andover, Revere—in addition to concerns about Ted, God help me—swirled through my brain. I'd been waiting too long for this. Never giving it a second-thought she might've been feeling the same way.

I slithered to the side of the mattress and admired the contours of Johanna's shape. The room's half-light and shadows gave her body's curves a surrealistic glow. I ran my fingers along Jo's shoulder . . . up her arm . . . to the small of her back, then lingered on the swell of her hips.

Johanna shivered. A slight moan spilled from her lips and I covered them with my own—only this time with a conscious attempt to lessen the pace, appreciate the moment I'd fantasized about for months by then.

I'd convinced myself Johanna had the sweetest breasts I would never get to taste. Sure, I had snuck glimpses of them that night at my mother's house when Jo had leaned forward and kissed me—wearing the half-opened and corny Wisconsin-themed bathrobe that her niece had given her. Then there were those naked self-portraits displaying Johanna in all her glory on the floor, propped against the walls of her Avon studio. Her body no longer out of reach, I buried my face in her chest and lovingly pushed her breasts together before bringing her nipples to my lips.

I was far from disappointed.

The sheen of her wet and glistening skin shimmered. I licked and nibbled Johanna's lower belly with delight, lingering momentarily on the scarcely visible scar that ran beneath short curls and across her soft mound. I lifted my head to kiss Johanna, and she placed her tongue into my welcoming mouth.

My hands continued to caress and explore.

Abruptly, Johanna stopped and backed away. "I'm a lot to deal with. Too intense. Too old. This can't possibly work."

She shimmied up and adjusted herself against the headboard.

Where was this coming from?

"Shssh." I put a finger to her lips before stroking her cheek and neck.

She hugged me.

Afraid—or too embarrassed—at first, Johanna refused to look at me. Then she drew back, held both of my arms. "It'll be wise to escape while you still can." A wry grin surfaced and quickly faded. "Sorry. I don't mean to be so bizarre."

Not quite non sequiturs, Johanna's rapid-fire admonitions flashed by like those impossible-to-decipher disclaimers spit out at hyper-speed during the conclusion of a commercial. Who ever pays attention to them?

I returned my finger to Jo's lips, then kissed her.

Soon, I rolled over, pulled Johanna on top of me, and entered—her heat searing and fervent.

Jo's lids were closed.

"Open your eyes, please."

Johanna had such stunning green eyes, and besides, I wanted her to witness my desire for her—how much I needed and craved this, craved *her*. Glinting in spots like tiny bits of sea glass reflecting from a placid and clear ocean floor, her eyes looked into mine.

She bent to kiss me, then arched backwards. A delicate smile danced across Johanna's face and masked any suffering she might've endured.

Al Green sang "Let's Stay Together" from a tape player, and I didn't care whether Jo's eyes remained opened or shut.

"We're gonna do this? Right?" She was referencing more than our lovemaking.

"Right?" she repeated—her voice clipped and elevated to a higher octave. "Right!" She panted a third time before I had an opportunity to answer—no longer a question, but an affirmation. Johanna's rhythm increased; her thrusting pulled me further inside. She tugged my shoulders to pry a response from me.

"Yes," I blurted out at last. Because some facet of me had been concentrating, trying to hold off. Trying to deny how incredibly turned on I was. Trying to remember. Thinking of all those tricks you read and heard about that were supposed to guide you in re-

137

sisting this avalanche of ecstasy. I struggled to focus on something else—anything other than me being deep within the scorching warmth of Johanna. *Jesus, can't you stop for a moment? Kiss her eyelids?* I asked myself. *Not too rough. Gentle. Gently. There now. OK. Check out those delightfully soft shoulders. How about the small of her back?*

Johanna had no interest in any of these diversions and when she stared and whispered, "Right?" again, I was lost. I couldn't exactly ask if she'd lift herself off of me, could I? *Just for a few minutes? I promise.* Or plead with her to stay absolutely still—*only for a couple of seconds?*

"Right!" Jo said, once more—now most definitely a command—before leaning forward and churning her hips, crushing them hard against me.

"Look at me, Matt."

Her sweet breasts brushed my face, and I sucked them.

Jo had no intention of engaging in non-verbal communication; she shook me and demanded to hear my voice.

"Right . . . RIGHT . . . *RIGHT*," I growled through gritted teeth and kissed Johanna's head.

Reefer smells from the Bottom Line crowd overtook the peach fragrance of her shampoo and mixed with our own verdant musk. I couldn't wait any longer. Was not able to help myself. I yearned to climb inside Johanna. And for some reason, I'd been holding my breath—as if that could've kept me from coming. Johanna blazed; heat surged up her belly and onto mine, and I had to remind myself to breathe because I didn't want to pass out. *And wouldn't that be embarrassing?* I mused. Soon, it didn't matter. Johanna hugged me, no longer rocking, nearly inert, only a steady-but-deliberate grinding. Visions of her cute butt bouncing on the saddle during that horseback ride in the Avon woods filled my thoughts.

"Don't stop. Please don't stop." She rubbed against me with intense pressure.

Johanna's nails dug into my shoulders. After the initial jolts of pain subsided, I only felt desire. It had been much too long. And I said "Oh God," followed by what might've been "I love you," then muttered, "Sorry" before everything burst from within.

Both of us held on to each other tight, striving to freeze the moment; but we gradually fell apart with yearning and despair.

Several minutes went by before I'd remembered Johanna had roommates.

I massaged her back and shoulders; then tenderly pulled her against my chest and groin. We spooned and tried to fall asleep. When her faint giggles waned, she sighed and our breaths slowed. Embracing Johanna closer, I glanced at prints on the wall and at her bookcases. For that night at least, I chose to believe the shelves of my past had been cleared—replaced by characters with tales full of hope and lacking backstory.

I woke, propped my head with one arm, and admired Johanna while she slept. Though more than grateful to be there, a minuscule part of me couldn't help think *it's about time*; it had been close to a year since that night we met at the Dylan concert.

When Johanna stirred, I slid between her thighs and nuzzled in the dampness of her silken hair.

Moments passed.

A shiver . . . a hint. Discovery and connection. Some muffled sighs.

Johanna caressed my forehead, tilted my chin in her direction, and murmured, "I need you inside me."

She clutched me against her. Thankful I'd been given a second chance, I thought—knew—I'd be capable of lasting longer this session; but Johanna rolled me over, climbed on top, and drove us home.

Afterwards, Jo rose to pee, and I clenched her hand. Astonished we were here at long last, I didn't want her to leave. When I finally let her go, she slipped a robe on—one without dairy cows and wedges of cheese. Its sleeve snagged the Sadat bobblehead resting on the bureau, and he nodded.

"Mornnnnn . . . ing," Louise grinned lasciviously—stretching the first syllable out forever. She'd already bought a couple of papers and handed me the *Soho News*.

Johanna and I spent the rest of the morning and early afternoon lying in bed, holding hands, and reading.

The mild December day provided us with the opportunity to walk to the West 4th Street Station—less than a half hour away—to get back to Penn.

"How are we going to make this work? I'm asking too much—you can't restrict yourself to me," she said.

I smiled, hoping Jo couldn't see my face. It wasn't as if I'd be relinquishing a booming social life in Boston. I turned and placed a finger to her lips.

At the subway, she started to speak, but oncoming metal wheels scraped against rails and the squealing howls muted her.

"We'll figure it out." I hugged Johanna before stepping off the platform and into the A train.

The doors closed. Little by little, I dropped my right hand onto the glass window, then waved goodbye.

— 19 —

I received the highly anticipated news that my search for a place to live had finally come to an end. The tours of "cozy"—translation: postage-stamp-size—Back Bay apartments led by my nice-enough granny-dressed real estate agent had grown stale, and I'd become discouraged by the stomping and light-switch-flipping tricks she employed to send cockroaches scurrying before she'd let me set foot inside a potential find. So, when she fell upon a spot on Newbury Street a couple hundred dollars over my budget but relatively clean and with more than one room, I jumped. The three-month temporary stay at my mother's had already been prolonged to five and then six; I would've never believed I'd miss living on my own so much.

Missing her bay windows, breathtaking vistas, high ceilings, and of course her, my apartment—on the third floor rear of a four-story brownstone—

couldn't touch Johanna's sixth-floor space. There were only four windows in this two-and-a-half room pad—two of which had steel bars on them, and a wrought iron emergency staircase framed another. My view—if you could call it that—consisted of a back alleyway for the row of buildings that fronted on Commonwealth Avenue. A woman who lived on the other side of the alley draped her laundry over fire escape railings—the scene reminiscent of those black-and-white '40s movies that featured inner-city life. Her drying bras, panties, and towels—so brazenly and wonderfully out of step with this posh neighborhood—served as a consistent reminder of my roots.

A dark blue rug, which must have been over forty years old, ran from the living room and spread—inexplicably—across the entire floor of my kitchen alcove. I might've removed this carpeting if I hadn't been in fear of what lay beneath. Green, severely chipped vinyl tiles covered the ample-sized bedroom. One of the electric stove burners didn't work and—uncertain if I'd ever get the oven to operate—I relied on a toaster model whenever I tackled a creative recipe or invited dinner guests over.

Yet, during most of those traditional New England winter days, when the comforting scent of lavender fabric softener wafted up my rear stairway from the commercial Laundromat in the basement, or on milder nights, when the oregano-seasoned aromas from tomato sauce simmering in the Italian restaurant a few doors down made their way through my barely opened windows, I was more than grateful once again to have landed somewhere I considered my own—no matter how many amenities it lacked. Although I would've loved it if something could've been done about the bathroom's outside walls, which sometimes got so cold the pipes froze.

Unlike the ascetic and unforgiving cement steps of Johanna's walk-up, my stairs—wooden and reeking of varnish—creaked and squawked with every step. Maybe that hadn't been such a bad thing. For much later, I'd wonder if Johanna's stairway was indicative of her difficult but steadfast quest to make a living there and if she'd unwittingly become an actor in that well-worn fable of the starving artist versus the stony city of New York.

— 20 —

The first housewarming gift I received—besides a box brimming with canned goods and sundry foodstuffs from my mother—was an original work of art by Johanna. Titled *Slow Train Coming*, it featured hand-painted reproductions of photos she'd taken of Dylan at the Hartford show. Placed on shroud-like soft fabric and washed in hues of purple, blue, pink, and yellow paint, the images—positioned on a fading crucifix—depicted a resurrection and reflected various stages of exposure so that in a few the singer was almost unrecognizable.

I resolved to make this nearly five foot tall by three foot wide painting the centerpiece of the apartment. A nonfunctioning fireplace stood in my living room. As sacrilege, someone had lacquered the gorgeously carved and natural wood that formed the mantel and frames in copious layers of thick white gloss. I bought an electric fireplace-log set at a thrift

146

shop near The Rat in Kenmore Square, then picked up a gallon of Sterling 5f5 paint remover—Orlando's recommendation—from the hardware store on Boylston Street. During the ensuing weeks, I devoted any spare time to stripping paint, eventually thrilled to discover the magnificent cherry wood that lay beneath it.

Mounting Jo's artwork over the fireplace pleased but also spooked me a bit. In some eerie way, it reminded me of a tiny chapel my grandmother had created in a small alcove of her home featuring a painting by my dad of a mother on her knees in a high-ceilinged cathedral. Teary-eyed, her hands stretched upward in search of her World War Two soldier son, whose helmeted image hovered from above. All that might've been missing from my own Newbury Street shrine was the plethora of plants Grandma cared for and the votive candles she lit every day of her life.

Along with her present, Johanna sent a card with *There goes the neighborhood* printed on its front. Gomez and Morticia Addams—holding wilted flowers—posed before their dilapidated and creepy Victorian and peered out from inside. A few pages of folded yellow legal-sized lined paper slipped to the floor when I opened it. I'd mailed Jo a clipping of my re-

147

cent Tom Waits concert review and several chapters of a novel I'd been working on sporadically during the previous year. She was effusive in her praise.

You made me believe I was sitting in the audience, she wrote. And later, Johanna told me she empathized with the anguish and stress the protagonist—a hospital nurse—had been going through. *I understood her trepidation and fear when she confronted those doctors with the truth. You captured the moment without being melodramatic.*

Biased certainly, but I couldn't remember anyone that close to me—other than a fellow workshop participant or teacher—affirming I might've possessed some level of talent. Johanna's response got me thinking about sixth grade and my "O Holy Night" solo at midnight Mass. Mary Jo Buchanon, two grades above me—and out of my reach in a thousand other ways—hugged me during the brief reception that followed the service and said, "You gave me chills." Then she added, "You look like Donny Osmond."

I'm not sure what compliment carried more weight at that stage; but it felt nice to matter.

Though already somewhat familiar with the neighborhood, on the weekend after the move, I embarked on a mini expedition. Deluca's Family Grocery stood to the left of my building, and one of at least five record stores within a three-block radius was on the right. The brownstone's entrance faced the Daisy Buchanan pub and, not far from there, on the same side of the street, was the original Emack & Bolio's ice cream parlor. A short walk on Fairfield Street led to two more record stores, Strawberries and New England Music City—and a 24-hour Star Market operated in the Prudential Center. The Trident, Harvard Bookstore Cafe, and Avenue Victor Hugo bookstores were only a few blocks from my place, and I'd pass a couple of video rental shops on the way to the Exeter Street Theater, at the next corner.

With all this and the many restaurants close by, there was little motive to own a car—or to leave the area. Weather permitting, I could walk to my recently found 11-to-7 night-shift job at the medical records department in Mass General Hospital—the primary reason I'd ended up in Back Bay.

On another exploratory jaunt some days later, I stepped into 33 1/3—the Indie record shop next door to my apartment. Almost closing time, most of the store's overhead lights were off and its track lighting had been dimmed. A desk-size disco ball—a relic from a *Saturday Night Fever* costume party, no doubt—projected a flash of colors across walls and ceiling. The dulcet tones of a mid-twenties auburn-haired woman behind the counter replaced those ridiculously distorted bass sounds you'd hear blasting from oversized speakers in nearby Tower and Strawberries. On the stereo, a synthesizer played repetitive arpeggio chords while the clerk sang along to Cyndi Lauper's ballad "All Through The Night." No wannabe, she belted out a stirring version, despite her pixie stature. Every once in a while, she mouthed the lyrics "we have no past" in my direction and punctuated her phrasing with a handheld label maker that snapped each time she stuck price tags on album covers. The woman even hit and held the coda's sustained notes that Lauper herself was known for.

I approached the register with Steve Forbert, Karla Bonoff, and other singer-songwriter records in my hands. She flipped both of her thumbs down and strode through the aisles, grabbing a Ramones album and an extended play disc from a local group called The Young Snakes.

"You can have the EP for free. Aimee, their bass player and lead singer, works at Newbury Comics. If you don't get into the other record, return it."

"I'm your new neighbor."

"Aubrey."

She lit an incense candle that smelled of cinnamon, excused herself, and walked away. A gurgling noise, which could've been from an electric mixer, blasted from the back room. Above a poster of Michael Jackson leaning against a red brick wall, a Foreigner mobile swung from the ceiling. Aubrey returned with two cups of espresso.

"Thanks. This is different." I took a sip.

"My mother's contraption. The only thing I snatched after she died. Can't say why. Didn't even know she had it."

Unconcerned her work day had long since passed, she spoke with me for more than an hour. At some point during our conversation, I gushed about Springsteen's double LP, *The River.*

"Angry people are not always wise," Aubrey said dismissively.

She made that statement with such authority that I waited for some attribution to follow and looked at her quizzically.

"*Pride and Prejudice.*" She pointed to a placard highlighting another work by Austen—an image from the BBC miniseries *Emma.* Handwritten in large letters beneath it was the quote: *Without music, life would be a blank to me.*

Then, she placed a Clash song on the turntable and sang something about "voices calling in my head," urging me to stop wasting time. Assuring me nothing—or "no one"—would be coming to save us.

This woman—who could cite Austen one moment and modern-day punk songs the next—reminded me of someone; though I couldn't figure out who. When I subsequently discovered she wrote a relationship/advice column for the *Phoenix*, it didn't surprise me.

It might've been due to the caffeine from the three or more espressos or the non-stop energy that emanated from Aubrey, but when I left the store, I'd already come to think of her as the Aurora Borealis of my neighborhood.

Three or four weeks went by before I met the couple who occupied the front apartment of our floor. A tall, preppy-looking guy about my age—squash racket in one hand—held the building's outside door open when he saw me saddled with groceries from DeLuca's. After I reached the top of the staircase, I set the bags down to fumble for my keys and he stretched out his hand to introduce himself.

"Marvin. Marvin Bush. You play?" He raised the

racket above his head before taking a few practice swings.

As it happened, I'd taken up the game a few months before after befriending David, a resident at Mass General. Eager to acquaint me with the joys of this sport and, more importantly, for him to keep in shape for the matches that mattered with senior members of the medical staff, he would've had me playing seven days a week if I had let him. With the ball—and rackets—being smaller than those employed in racket ball, squash seemed a safer option for me. And I intended to assist David in navigating the hospital hierarchy, even if that meant he had to master smacking a tiny sphere against an impervious surface rather than learning to take better care of his patients. We might not have played as frequently as David wanted, but got together often enough. Still, I never imagined I'd ever rise above subpar.

I visited Johanna at least a couple of weekends per month. With her roommates' approval—and a few hundred dollars more we contributed monthly for the rent—she designed the alcove where the sofa bed sat as a sort of study. Two of my favorite pieces of hers hung on the wall: a pastel self-portrait and a landscape painting, completed when she studied in

153

France. Johanna informed me confidently that this space was where I would begin my version of the great American novel.

And Jo attempted to travel to Boston once each month.

During a more noteworthy stay, Johanna learned she'd drawn the short straw in reciprocal accommodations when she couldn't get the shower to function and ran out into the living room in the chill of a February morning for help. I obliged by snatching the towel wrapped around her, nudging us towards a $99 sofa bed I'd picked up at Bob's Discount on Revere Beach, and making love. Later, I plugged in a hair dryer, aimed it at the exterior wall, and showed Jo how she would periodically have to warm the bathroom pipes in order to trigger water flow again.

"You did that on purpose!" Johanna accused me of intentionally letting the pipes freeze so she'd have to seek my assistance while half naked.

"Never."

She smiled, and all pretense of anger dissipated.

We rationalized to each other that meeting for two, sometimes three, quality weekends a month accounted for much more time than many married Yuppie couples got to see each other.

When months passed, and it became clear Johanna hoped to maintain this schedule, I got in touch with my brother to ask if he could find someone to cover for him at the gas station he owned and help me construct a platform bed.

The plywood had to be pre-cut into three sections before we could lug it up the stairway, and my recently purchased mattress ended up requiring its own trick. On that occasion, we recruited Marvin, and the three of us bent and manipulated it through the hallway and into the apartment door.

Orlando had recommended this type of bed because it would be the less expensive alternative. And, during a previous visit, he realized a double-sized box spring would never have made it up those front stairs, and I would've had to hire a crane for the back alley and remove a window—as I'd done for my upright piano. The notion of going through that ordeal once more didn't thrill me—although the company's name, Death Wish Movers, continued to bring a smile to my face.

I appreciated the rare opportunity to spend time with my older brother, who worked with tools and associated implements that came with alien names like socket wrench, miter saw, carpenter square, and Phillips drill bits. Orlando employed the precision and pride of craft a surgeon might have and exhibited a patience I so wished my dad had possessed.

When I was about thirteen or fourteen, my father demolished a closet next to our kitchen. After having strung together several decent tile jobs in a row, he'd bought a new washer and dryer for my mother and planned to install them in this room. Orlando wasn't home that day—Dad usually enlisted my brother for those types of tasks. So he was stuck with me.

He'd already knocked down the walls with a sledgehammer and dragged most of the debris out to a rented dumpster crammed in the yard. Chunks of plaster and thin wooden slats covered the floor; dust hung in the air. My father wanted me to help him "sweat" the pipes. This, he explained, was the method plumbers used to connect two sections of copper pipe. I held the ends on top of a cinder block while he sliced them with a hacksaw into appropriately sized pieces. Then Dad took sandpaper and smoothed the metal burrs on each side.

He placed the pipes about four feet high against the wall to make sure he'd cut them to the correct dimensions. "Hold tight. Don't let it move."

He put a fitting over one end, unrolled a spool of solder, and lit a propane torch. I watched hypnotized as its yellow and red flame transformed to a deep blue; solder melted and dripped.

"Steady," he warned me.

Slowly, the pipe twisted, slipped, and then dis-engaged from its fitting—plunging sharply; the fiery side then bounced off my hand, singeing the top of my wrist.

My father lunged for the pipe instinctively, burned the tips of his fingers, and tossed it away.

"God dammit. Can't you do anything right?!"

I raced out to the backyard and our garden hose.

The patch of skin where the pipe fell had turned scarlet and bubbled up before I sprayed cold water on it. I lingered for a good while, waiting for my dad to follow me outside and let me know if his own hand was OK. When it became clear he wouldn't be coming, I walked out of our yard and across the street to the Indian Trail.

Orlando had performed the preliminary work for my bed in a shed alongside his gas station; he'd cut several pieces of lumber—besides the plywood—in various shapes and sizes. I helped him place each "foot" while he bolted them to two-by-fours. He painstakingly showed me how to read the bubbles correctly on a level—a task I knew must've been ele-mentary—and screwed four metal braces to what would be corners of the bed. If my inadequate skills and knowledge exasperated him—which they must have—Orlando never let on.

He would've been justified if he'd said, "Matt, you're in your twenties. How do you not know this stuff?" But admonishments never escaped his lips. As he transitioned from the *Racing Form, Boston Herald* and maybe a Robert Parker *Spenser* novel to works by Ram Dass and books with *Buddha* in the titles, I continued to razz him without letting up. Yet, truth be told, he'd become the most centered and reliable person I'd known; I both envied that about him and remained indebted to it.

Orlando attached a spindle-like structure to the frame's edge. About twelve inches tall, with twirls on them, they resembled the soft-serve ice cream cones we devoured as kids while sitting at Dairy Queen on Broadway in Revere. "Turned them with a lathe."

I nodded in acknowledgement—although I didn't understand what he meant.

Orlando motioned for me to pass him a socket wrench and the drill so he could attach a few more "galvanized-steel" brackets.

"They'll provide extra support."

When he pointed out why, I once again lamented the fact Dad didn't have the tolerance to teach me any aspect of the tile trade. Orlando proved a quick study while I'd never gained the focus our father demanded.

My brother apologized for the furniture's "down and dirty" nature. "It's rough. If I had time and could do more in my garage, I would've added a couple of storage drawers beneath it."

Orlando explained he would have "finished this" or "mitered that." I couldn't retain much of it though—the lexicon still foreign to me.

"It's fine. It works. I'm thrilled and I'm sure Johanna will be ecstatic. She's grown weary of sleeping on the floor."

We spread old newspapers onto the vinyl tiles. Orlando handed me a paintbrush, pried the lid off a can, and we covered the wood with a light stain.

Before long, I opened as many apartment windows as I could to allow fresh air to circulate.

"That's potent," I said.

"Sorry. This is another thing I would've done before I came here. And could have—if you weren't hoping to have things ready by the weekend."

The night ended over some Miller beers from a six-pack he'd brought. During our conversation, Orlando asked me at least three times if I was "alright" between his prodding for me to share "the scoop on the new babe."

My face lit up, I'm certain, when I described Johanna's talent.

"Yeah, but what does she look like?" A smirk fled the right side of his mouth.

I said something about Jo's button nose, Wisconsin accent, and the locks of hair constantly falling in front of her left eye that she refused to cut.

"She's a weird dresser, though."

"When did you turn into a fashion expert?" Orlando flicked at the collar of my dark turtleneck jersey.

He grinned and shook his head, then took a swig of beer before heading for the door. Turning around, he smiled.

"What?" I said.

"Never remember seeing you this happy."

I walked Orlando down the stairs, out to his truck, and repeatedly tried to slip a hundred dollars into his hand before giving in to his refusals.

"Next visit, I'll help you get rid of that bargain basement sofa. And replace that shitty bedroom floor while we're at it." My brother waved before driving off.

— 21 —

Johanna slept on our new bed during a visit to attend Judy Chicago's *Dinner Party* exhibition. On the night before the show, we lay under the covers and read. Before long, she headed for the bathroom and, after returning, hovered above me, paused, then planted a deep and prolonged kiss on my lips before climbing in.

"Wow. Thanks. What's that for?"

"Do you realize what a pain it's been for me to climb off the mattress to pee? I'm not sure how much longer my back could've taken it."

Sometimes, it really is the little things.

Johanna's reaction to the *Dinner Party* was similar to that conversation in the Surf Maid after we saw the *Daughters of Chaos* movie; Chicago's art installation celebrated the female spirit, but more so. One critic, a woman, hailed it as "heroic."

Yet judging by the tone of snarky reviews—written by men mostly—an event lauding woman-kind for their myriad overlooked accomplishments and contributions was unnecessary and pointless—even vulgar. It seemed to me a lot of the apparent controversy had to do with guys feeling threatened. Who and what were these threats? The artists? Their work? The facts?

True, the vaginas—those so-called "flower imag-es"—were definitely and unmistakably in your face. "A muff-diver's paradise," my childhood friend Damian might have crudely termed it. Rather than center on some of the obvious anger and militancy, though, I focused on the project's celebratory aspects and the humor inherent in the heavy dose of male discomfort it brought. After forcing women to suffer through centuries of phallic symbols, what harm could thirty-nine vulva-covered dinner plates, some postcards, and a few commemorative t-shirts possibly do?

That a project of this scale had never been con-sidered before was heartbreaking. Johanna had told me Janson's *History of Art*—the hefty tome that I, along with several hundred thousand other college freshman had been assigned—did not mention a sin-gle female artist in its six hundred plus pages. This made me wonder if I was living in the *nineteen-eighties*.

Chicago's initial vision—to present an alternative interpretation of the *Last Supper*—stationed women at the table and emphasized their achievements as well as their history of oppression and confinement. This concept expanded into a forty-eight-foot table that included two thousand three hundred hand-made tiles, place settings for thirty-nine women, with close to a thousand more being inscribed on the "Heritage Floor."

Though unfamiliar with the vast majority of artists represented in *The Dinner Party*, I did have a cursory knowledge of Emma Goldman, Susan B. Anthony, Florence Nightingale, the Brontë sisters and even knew something about Mary Wollstonecraft and her *Vindication of the Rights of Woman.* Johanna possessed a deeper insight into many more; but it would've been an impossible task for anyone to be familiar with them all.

We meandered through the exhibit space and Johanna drew on her teaching skills, expounding on the merits of Hypatia—a child prodigy of the Roman Empire and eventually the head of the University of Alexandria. "A threat to Christians because of her support for education, she ended up being viciously murdered by fanatical monks," Jo said.

She also spoke of Artemisia Gentileschi, a rape survivor who endured a farce of a trial. Johanna looked up from the setting created for Gentileschi, saying, "Yet she became one of the most respected painters of her era."

I pointed out a table runner that appeared wrinkled to me.

Johanna's eyes lit up. "That's no accident."

She took my hand. "See the way the cloth circles and almost overwhelms the plate? It represents the struggle female artists faced. *Face*."

Johanna led me to the Elizabeth Blackwell section. "Notice how the forms are drawing away from the edges and borders? That symbolizes the breaking of barriers."

Though not sure I understood the nuances, the hints of significance, Jo helped me to look at the remaining settings differently. I didn't feel as lost somehow.

"Blackwell was the first woman to graduate from med school and become a licensed female doc," Johanna said. And, I gleaned from the exhibit later, she had been *ridiculed, spat on and refused space to rent and set up shop. So she opened a clinic to treat and educate women on sex, birth, and other health issues.*

Johanna continued to share additional details about the talents, trials, and resourcefulness of these women in such a gracious and non-condescending manner that soon a few other people followed us as if she might've been an official tour guide for the *Party*. She spoke in such a conversational tone I could imagine what the experience must have been like for her students when she taught at the university.

Jo beamed when a number of new disciples gathered round. While she discussed elements of the project with them, I snuck off and viewed sections that focused on writers Rebecca West and Dorothy Richardson, musician Mary Lou Williams, and filmmaker Maya Deren.

"What's the big deal?" a dapper man in bow tie said to me at the setting for Emily Dickinson.

I paused for a moment. The guy seemed sharp enough. Would it have made any sense to try to convince him? Was it my role to do so?

I considered telling him I'd been enjoying myself and had welcomed any excuse to be with Johanna. Why should it have mattered to me what this person thought about Chicago, female artists—or us?

Before I could speak, he said, "We've bartered. I sit through this and my wife says we can see *Conan the Barbarian*."

"Schwarzenegger is great, I've heard," Johanna said after sneaking up from behind. I took her hand, and we kissed before walking off.

After making it downstairs to the hallway, we edged towards the exit. Dozens of people—including the two of us—passed a cleaning woman pushing her cart and attempting to gain headway in the opposite direction. Folks from all walks of life dressed in everything from beaded bell bottoms, tie-dyed peace-symbol-emblazoned t-shirts, and full tuxes, jostled and shoved—forcing her to abandon the cart and hug the wall. The only one to stop, turn around, and help the woman navigate that throng was Johanna. She broke away, stood next to her until the bulk of the crowd dispersed, then took the woman's keys, unlocked an office door and wheeled her stuff through.

I waited near the building's front entrance and, after a few minutes, when Johanna returned to my side, I learned the woman's children were still in Ghana and she hoped to have them join her one day.

That night, we browsed through a Boylston Street card shop, Copley Flair—a cute bit of wordplay on Copley Square. Johanna found a few pairs of Boston-themed socks, which featured Tea Party ships—"For my niece," she said—and also bought a handful of postcards. I got a key chain to give to Jo later—along with the key to my place—a gesture long overdue. To hide it from her during checkout, I slipped it between the pages of an embossed journal I'd picked up.

At my apartment, Jo taped a postcard to my bedroom mirror—a picture of a sun-glassed John Lennon with arms folded and wearing an "I love New York" t-shirt. On the flip side, with every letter in caps, she wrote, *WISH YOU WERE HERE! LOVE JO.*

When I put the key ring in her palm, she kissed me before saying, "It's about time."

Another of Johanna's "wired" nights—as I'd dubbed them—followed. No matter how hard I tried, I couldn't damper her enthusiasm or settle her down. We made love twice, and I believed I'd satisfied her; yet Johanna pushed for a third time—her energy and passion unrelenting. Despite the flattered and willing state of my spirit, the flesh refused to be convinced.

So Jo rose from our bed and watered the plants— although I'd reminded her I'd done it the day before. She washed the few remaining dishes we'd left in the sink and emptied crumbs from the toaster oven. Soon Johanna rearranged glassware in the kitchen cabinet—taller glasses in the rear, shorter ones in front. She'd gathered the bathroom towels, placed them in a laundry basket and would have headed to the Laundromat in the basement had I not taken the basket from her, dropped it on the couch, and gently guided her to the bedroom.

After I massaged her back for an extended period, she finally relaxed and fell asleep.

In the movie *When Harry Met Sally*, Harry claimed when you drove with a lover to the airport, it was a sure sign of the beginning of a new relationship. So he told Sally he never accompanied a woman on those trips because he didn't want to be asked later why he no longer traveled with her to meet the flight.

I still escorted Johanna to the train station or airline terminal. But understood why someone might not wish to do so, and it had nothing to do with Harry's hypothesis.

Those excursions to Logan—or to South and Penn stations—were becoming too much. Tiring and stressful events aggravated by harried commutes and nearly missed departures, they'd also turned melancholic—despite any fun we might've had. Quality time notwithstanding, we discovered you didn't have to be a math whiz to figure out five to six days a month would never add up to a week.

Some connections don't require proximity. But Johanna's and my relationship suffered from the damage distance brought, as well as other impediments that had little to do with the two hundred twenty-one physical miles that separated us.

On our cab ride to the airport that weekend of *The Dinner Party*, I let Johanna know I'd scored some tickets to an upcoming Blondie concert for her return visit.

She sneered. "Exploitation in all its glory. Sex sells records."

A limited view—even for Johanna, I reasoned.

"Have you bothered to listen to the band? They're fantastic."

"And I bet you don't mind that Debbie Harry is braless while they're selling it."

"Jesus. Does every form of entertainment have to be a fucking statement, a feminist treatise?"

I liked the fact Harry didn't always wear a bra— she had a nice shape, after all.

"Am I supposed to turn and look the other way? It also doesn't bother me when she writhes and sings 'In the Flesh.' Does that make me a bad person?"

Johanna looked out the taxi window, put her fingers on the glass, and shook her head.

I sometimes wondered, if we could have gone to

169

a few more movies like *Tootsie* and *Somewhere in Time*—instead of *My Brilliant Career, El Norte,* and those other indie films—would circumstances have been different? Would Johanna have been able to pause, catch a breath, and learn to enjoy things—simply for pleasure's sake—and then somehow realize her life's journey did not have to take place on a single set of tracks leading in one direction without spurs, stops, or delays? Maybe there'd even be a minor derailment or two encountered along the way.

"Wouldn't it be pretty to think so?"—to paraphrase Hemingway and repeat something Orlando said frequently.

For I was just about certain that as the rest of us played in our sandboxes and climbed jungle gyms, Johanna had been sitting alone in a schoolyard corner diligently working on a watercolor painting of flowers that sprouted from her kindergarten's window box—the ticket to her destiny already punched.

I reached out to hold Johanna's hand—surprised she allowed me to.

We rode in silence, the weekend now behind us, and I thought of the previous night. While we'd waited for our order in Emack & Bolio's, two kids pulled and twisted a long piece of pink taffy between them. The melting candy stretched and drooped in precarious ways and morphed into strange shapes— almost separating. More than a few times, it nearly grazed the scarred and sullied wooden floor.

— 22 —

At first, we phoned each other almost daily. Sometimes we'd mention a song heard that day, a passage from a book recently read, a sketch Jo had started, or perhaps a paragraph or two of fiction I'd written, revised, and later felt good about. The purpose of these calls was nothing more than to be treated to the elixir of each other's voices.

There were times, though, my conversations with Johanna would baffle me. One night, she spoke about the "peace project" she'd been working on.

"I can only conjure up violent images—the *anti*-peace." She laughed wearily. "So, I found myself drawing tanks and guns and fists. Then painting large X's across them with thick dripping brush strokes."

"Jo—" I said.

"—Dark. Dark. Dark. I stood back and examined them, you know? And it was as if I'd painted a bunch of giant 'Do Not Litter' signs—"

"Hon—"

"—You've seen the type; the ones skirting the sides of highways. That show crumbled paper with a diagonal slash over them?"

"Johanna. Maybe every work doesn't have to be—or begin—on such a grand scale."

Short gasps of breath whispered through the line. I wondered if she was hyperventilating or possibly crying.

"Jo?"

"Yes," she said softly.

"How about starting with a traditional symbol?... A dove? Two people holding hands—a bright candle piecing the darkness?"

"Nah—that's old hat."

I offered alternate visions—like a simple baby's smile. But either she didn't hear me—or had regained a second wind.

"Encourage one another. Be of one mind. Live in peace and the God of love. And peace will be with you . . ." Johanna's voice trailed off.

"Huh?"

"From Corinthians. What Sister Joan used to say. You don't understand."

"Let me try."

"You'll never—you're not an artist."

I placed the phone on speaker, stormed the few steps towards my kitchen alcove, removed clean dishes from the strainer, dumped them into the empty sink, and washed them all over again. In my childhood home, the volume of clanging silver and tableware was directly proportional to the level of anger. That night, the decibel scale reached record heights. This had no effect on Johanna.

I could never figure out the origins of her tirades—if they had been triggered by exhaustion, alcohol, insecurity . . . or worse. At some point—about the time I put on a pot of coffee—she referred to me as "just a man."

I picked up the handset, stretched out on that shabby blue carpet, and stared at Johanna's mounted Dylan shroud. An hour, maybe two, passed; beams of sunlight trickled through the edges of my window blinds and—true to form—Jo wound down. I had learned to wait it out—not hang up too quickly—for fear of recrimination certainly, but also, dread of something graver. For Johanna could descend to such gloomy depths during these conversations littered with so many acquiescent *it doesn't matters* that I sometimes had genuine concern for what she might do to herself.

The next day, Jo apologized profusely. These phone calls—full of regret—would occasionally be accompanied by her singing some sort of ballad. Other times, Johanna remembered little from a previous night's chat—as though she woke suffering from amnesia after careening off a dark highway and she'd become disoriented, wondering how she ended up in the ditch.

And I was the AAA service guy she called for help.

Some of those nightly exchanges with Johanna reminded me of the plaintive bells Salvation Army volunteers jingled at store-fronts during Christmastime: I knew I should, but couldn't possibly offer a donation every time I crossed their paths. So now and then I'd lose patience, slink away and hunt for a different means of escape.

But Jo could redeem herself. Like the weekend she visited and insisted on bringing me to dinner. We'd cut down eating in restaurants because I preferred cooking a meal or ordering take out so we could be alone as much as possible. On that day, Jo was adamant.

As soon as we got to my pad from South Station, Johanna hustled to the shower and changed not once, but three times. First, she came out of the bedroom in

Jordache dress jeans and a pastel-colored hand-painted blouse. She ambled past me, and stood before an intricately bordered mirror which, at her suggestion, I'd bought at a yard sale and hung on the wall to make the room "appear larger."

"What do you think?"

"You look great. Let's go."

Johanna had made reservations for 7:30 and the restaurant was a half dozen subway stops from my apartment.

"I'll be right back."

Jo returned with a blue striped long-sleeved shirt of mine that she often liked to sleep in.

"Fine. That looks sharp. Come on." I nodded my head towards the front entrance in a futile attempt to convince her.

"Not dressy enough."

"The place is casual," I said through the closed door. "It doesn't matter." *Shit*, I whispered—realizing I should've kept that last remark to myself. "It's getting late. Should I call a cab?"

Finally, she paraded by wearing a flowing, full-length, rose-covered summer dress and I was no longer pissed she'd made me wait.

"Ravishing."

I leaned in to kiss her.

To reach the Scotch & Sirloin—on the seventh floor of a renovated warehouse—we had to take an ancient self-service open-barred wrought iron freight elevator. Because of my fear of heights, it intimidated me—and Jo wasn't too enthused by the loud clang of its gated doors and the death-rattle shakes that marked each successive level as we climbed. She clung to me when we rose higher—using it as an excuse to run a hand under my shirt along my naked back and slip her other down the front of my pants.

Thank God we're alone, I thought, growing more grateful for archaic and rickety elevators.

Throughout the restaurant, exposed duct work flanked various sections of ceiling. Pieces of factory machinery replete with their associated belts perched in corners while light bulbs from solitary cords loomed above.

We sat by the windows and found menus printed in white lettering atop retro metal lunch boxes. I ordered steak; Johanna had shrimp and lots of other stuff from the salad bar. A black and blue sky framed her face while cars racing north and south streamed lights across an elevated expressway. Jo looked exquisite—grinning like a person who'd been privy to a secret that had somehow infused her with happiness; I wanted to freeze time.

177

Sparklers on a cake headed in our direction and reflected off windows; waiters sang "Happy Birthday." Since mine was not for a few weeks, I figured they'd been walking to a table nearby. But Johanna's canary-swallowing smile grew wider, the guys stopped, and she asked me to make a wish.

My wishes had already come true, I reasoned, but blew the candles out anyway.

After finishing dessert, she suggested we have a drink in the lounge next door and I discovered this was only the start of her birthday surprises for the night. The club featured live bands some days and a disk jockey spinning records on others. Johanna arranged to have the DJ play an entire forty-minute set of several of my favorite songs. She and I nursed a couple of drinks and even fit in a slow dance to some sappy Neil Diamond ballad. I slid my hand to the small of Jo's back—her dress fabric so flimsy my fingers felt as if they were caressing exposed skin.

We hailed a taxi, settled on the couch at home, and kissed until Johanna got up abruptly, telling me she had to change.

Again? I fretted.

She returned draped in a negligee I later learned she'd picked out at a chic Newbury Street lingerie shop during a previous visit. An alley streetlamp shone through the window; it back-lit the diaphanous material and accentuated the soft contours of Johanna's hips. A shadow crossed her face and chest; and for a moment, she appeared to be divided in half. Jo knelt on the carpet, pulled a record from an album sleeve, and placed it on the turntable. With stereo needle raised, she locked her eyes with mine and said, "Any requests?"

I had only one.

I took Johanna by the hand and led her to the bedroom.

A long-distance relationship is never simple, however. Although neither of us expressed this in so many words, we both sensed our journey being thrown off course. Or its momentum had stalled—stymied by spats in sad cab rides en route to the airport that had now become the norm, and still more wired phone calls. No amount of late night crooning would save that.

Perhaps because of my selfishness and detachment—my tendency to love behind safe and reserved barriers—I sometimes viewed Johanna's behavior as a form of emotional monopoly or greed. That she was willing to bare everything unnerved me.

I wished I could be that open, that free.

Ultimately, guilt crept in. If I couldn't be there for Jo to lean on, who would be?

These turbulent phases kept recurring—familiar, no longer unexpected, and a part of our package. Like the Fox River canal system in Appleton that Johanna had described long before, I'd discover Jo a lock or more ahead of me and I'd continue to paddle—desperately trying to reach her.

Frustrated one night, when Johanna told me she was overwhelmed, I defensively made the case for backing off—rather than offer to spend time with her. "Maybe we should take a break."

Two days later, she called in tears.

"It has nothing to do with you," she assured me, but couldn't—or wouldn't—provide further clarification.

I felt as though I were watching a foreign movie bereft of subtitles; captivated yet bewildered, could I still be blamed if I didn't understand?

When I was a kid, my grandfather stocked several sparkling aquariums with an assortment of colorful tropical fish. In one tank, a brilliant rainbow Platy couldn't regulate her position. She'd struggle to the surface, shimmy furiously to regain equilibrium, before sinking back down to the bottom and resting on gravel. Then she'd repeat these efforts all over again.

"Swim bladder disease."

My grandfather pronounced the diagnosis without a hint of emotion.

As the months passed, on our good—or even great—days, a storm loomed on the horizon and veered in our direction; we had to somehow keep it at bay. I pondered what Johanna had said after viewing the art in the Addison Gallery: "How will I get there?"

I couldn't figure out what this destination of Johanna's entailed. Wherever we went, I saw how Jo supported other artists, truly encouraged them; it was never a contest with her. She once asked a young sculptor and painter at an exhibition of hers in the Village what they were working on and then spent close to an hour focusing on *their* projects and goals—practically ignoring the folks who had come to visit her.

Some kind of competition raged deep within her though.

On occasion, an intense phone conversation of ours would make me late for my shift, and that pissed me off. Inevitably, I'd be disappointed with my response. The impetus and demons that drove Jo were palpable—whatever they were. Without fail, she'd send a follow-up card or letter full of contrition—often shame—after these incidents.

My dad once said, "Couples aren't supposed to be therapists for one another."

I ignored him.

Later, I came to understand what he meant. A lover never aspired to play the role of therapist. Now and then, it became a thin and indistinguishable line between the two.

Johanna had no desire for therapy from me, but did seek an "all in" commitment. The "real thing" she once called it.

There were instances I convinced myself Johanna purposely pursued despair in order to jumpstart artistic inspiration. Especially when that technique proved successful and she would withdraw, dive into a project, growing silent and dark—a shuttered store at closing time—making me feel as necessary as a snow shovel on the shores of Miami Beach.

This dance of ours spurred at least one series: *Manscapes*, some of whose subjects bore a striking and unflattering resemblance to me. Guys reached out toward the viewer with arms lacking hands; one Magritte-style piece showed a pie where the figure's heart should've been. There were musical notes in place of brains, manuscript pages containing only ellipses. Then passion was depicted—smoke, fire, sun, water, thriving plants—and naked men on horses, with chests larger than I could've ever dreamed of. I disregarded what Johanna had taught me at the *Dinner Party* show and left the interpretation to others.

So, despite the bumps and massive potholes before us, we neglected highway signs and continued the ride in our vintage Rolls Royce. But now we'd gotten stuck in the UK—with a standard transmission—and I was being forced to drive on the opposite side of the road, to places that weren't on the map. I still hoped—believed—we could get closer, reach a deeper connection in spite of the near misses and collisions we were sure to face along the way.

— 23 —

Johanna teamed up with a performance artist she befriended in the Village to start Manhattan Magic, a joint venture, making fiber art—blouses, dresses, skirts—with hand-painted designs inscribed on them.

I'd met Katey, Jo's friend, at a show of hers several months before. In it, a half dozen nude women, with triangular patches of opaque gauze placed over their genitals and flesh-colored makeup covering their nipples, rolled six mannequins out on wheels. The plastic figures, in every shape and size, sported natural-looking underarm and pubic hair and were graced with lifelike rosy and brown shaded nipples.

Sheena Easton's "Strut," Helen Reddy's "I Am Woman," and tunes of that ilk blared in the background. Mini floodlights crisscrossed the room—washing ceilings and windows—while other lamps shimmered, illuminating the space like a dance hall.

Though the militancy of a few had me a bit on edge—especially after some scowls were sent my way—most of the women tried to put me at ease and approached the event with humor rather than anger. After discovering I was one of the few men present, a woman somehow managed to remove her bra through her sleeves without ever having to take her jersey off. Then she autographed it with lipstick, smiled, and handed it over, before fading into the crowd. Later, another gave me a cold bottle of beer. I'd never been to Mardi Gras, but those revelers helped me envision what that festival must be like.

After the first group of performers retreated to a back room, an elderly custodian—looking puzzled—edged a trash bin resting upon a two-wheeler to the far end of the open space. Soon, one more ensemble of women entered. They pulled wagons, pushed wheelchairs and wheelbarrows full of molded body parts and prosthetics—arms, legs, torsos, hands, and feet.

For the finale, a naked woman—swathed only in a large American flag and wearing a crown of thorns—shoved a shopping cart into a corner. It contained pumpkins covered by wigs and painted with mascaraed eyes and lipstick. She tossed these replica heads into the air and whacked them with a baseball bat down the long corridor near the bewildered janitor.

Pieces of fruit—along with hairpieces of all shapes, colors, and sizes—splattered in different directions before smashing onto the floor. It was as if a Rene Magritte painting had turned ripe and met up with several characters from *Dawn of the Dead*. When the man moved his barrel to the middle of the room and swept up the mess, he reminded me of the mustached cartoon character who cleaned up with a push broom at the conclusion of each *Fractured Fairytale* episode.

Johanna grinned throughout the performance. "Well?" she said afterwards.

"I'm not sure what to think." This wasn't entirely true.

"It's how you *feel* that matters."

I kissed Johanna, avoiding the need to provide her with an answer.

A few months after that, when she invited me to Katey's next gig, I politely declined.

Jo and her partner found a distributor, and a Faneuil Hall Market boutique shop—about three miles from my place on Newbury—offered to sell samples of their handiwork.

During one of Johanna's visits, when we browsed through that store, I was awed by the beauty of the Manhattan Magic dresses on display. For the first time though, Jo noticed the incredible markup and this distressed her. On average, she and Katey split twenty-two dollars per item, but no garment hanging on the racks of these shops was priced below ninety-five dollars.

During a pizza lunch at The European in Boston's North End, I strove to buoy Johanna's spirits, with little success. When we returned to my apartment, she thumbed through the *Real Paper* and learned that *The War at Home*, a movie about her alma mater, the University of Wisconsin in Madison, was scheduled to be featured as a select screening at the Exeter Street Theater.

"We should go," she said.

Not exactly the best method of cheering you up, I thought, but then mistakenly blurted out loud.

"I appreciate it, Matt. Though it's not your job to play my court jester."

Before we headed to the Exeter, Johanna shared tales of her participation in the women's and Black movements on campus. She spoke of protests against Dow chemical which had manufactured napalm and

Agent Orange during the Vietnam War, and had also recruited at the college. Had this activism contributed to the disconnect she'd been feeling in other parts of her life—wrongs she'd hoped to right?

This was personal to Johanna; the film's politics were not the only elements that struck a chord with her. She'd lived through it. I had remembered she'd gone to UW-Madison, but an additional current of energy buzzed through Johanna that night, and I couldn't fathom what it meant. Instead of her customary response to these types of events—edging forward towards the stage—Jo leaned backwards and gripped my hand.

During a preliminary scene when I saw a war protestor's sign—"WOMEN SAY YES TO MEN WHO SAY NO", I grinned—but was soon overcome by raw images of blood spilling from the various body wounds and cracked foreheads of students. Many of those traumatized skulls I'd viewed—and the betrayed girlfriends duped by undercover cops and FBI agents pretending to be their lovers—could've been Johanna's friends, could've been her.

I strained to find Johanna in crowds on the screen and searched for glimpses of her in candlelight vigils where people carried names of dead soldiers on placards overhead and read their corresponding cities aloud.

These movie frames clashed with the polished and austere splendor of the Richardsonian Romanesque Exeter Theater—nearly one hundred-years-old—and its ornate furnishings. I looked up at the looming stained-glass windows and prayed—for who or what, I wasn't certain. This was no buttered popcorn and soda matinee.

Johanna was so far ahead. Would I ever catch up? Too much time had passed before I'd acknowledged the schisms troubling our country. Things hadn't dawned on me until the '68 Chicago convention. Three months before then, in seventh grade, I'd delivered an essay in defense of the "domino theory" as justification for our involvement in Vietnam. For that argument—presented in front of a school assembly—I'd won an award at St Mary's. This junior high achievement contrasted starkly against Johanna's enlightenment and combat in the trenches; I still felt embarrassed, inadequate.

When Sister Rosanne encouraged me to prepare a book report on Dick Gregory's memoir during finals that semester, I was grateful. Though I ended up with a draft card a few years later, I lucked out because of a high lottery number; so I was able to avoid action or—more significantly—a decision concerning what to do if drafted. But for most kids in my inner city and in Black communities, student deferments, or a trip to Canada, remained unrealistic options.

That evening in the Exeter, I watched as Johanna's customarily even breathing quickened—her chest heaved during portions of the movie and it occurred to me it could have been called "The War *Within*."

After the final strains of Jefferson Airplane's "We Can Be Together" played over the closing credits and the screen went black, feet shuffled, seats flapped and echoed throughout the stunned hall. Johanna and I walked out without speaking; we were not alone. No one else seemed to be talking.

I led us the long way home to my apartment— south along Newbury, down to the corner of Dartmouth, up to Boylston . . . several blocks north to Mass Ave, and back towards Newbury again. Wind gusts hurled plastic bags from Bonwit Teller; they wrapped around our ankles before breaking free. A cardboard cup rolled and shuddered at the edge of a street before it popped against the curb; Magic Pan napkins fluttered and swirled in the breeze. We passed a life-sized advertisement featuring a couple promoting a neighborhood optical shop. A woman with a million-dollar smile huddled close to her guy; they both sported large-framed glasses. *Since when did glasses get hip?* I wondered—remembering my tormented "coke bottle" lens days before I'd gotten fitted for contacts. At Emack & Bolio's, we stopped to decompress and struggled through snippets of conversation—any silence understood, not awkward.

When we approached my building, two well-dressed men wearing earphones guarded the entrance. I'd been through this drill before and asked Johanna to take out her ID. One man recognized me, glanced at Jo's license, then held the door open for us. At the top of the landing stood a stocky white-haired lady with Marvin—his mother, the Vice President's wife.

"You didn't have to go through all this trouble for me," Johanna said, with weary sarcasm.

We stripped and crawled under the covers.

Johanna turned and ran her fingers through my chest hair. "Hold me. Just hold me. Please."

I drew Jo closer until she rested her head on me and, before long, fell asleep.

On my bedroom wall hung one of Johanna's paintings—bright waves of pinks, oranges, and blues with a flurry of stars in different sizes and shapes. Jo had transformed several canvases into mythical battlefields. Rather than slay dragons, her goal was to vanquish negativity in belief and deed. In this piece, the lighter-brushed shades of orange appeared to be defeating the painterly, broader blues. Were the various stars surrounding them a sign of victory? Or, like in those old *Tom & Jerry* cartoons, merely symbolic representations of repeated blows to the skull?

Johanna's recurrent question, "How will I get there?" circled and riddled my thoughts—like the stars in her painting. And I wondered if Jo hadn't been striving to reach some place in the future all along—but a location from her past, a person who she once was, one she had been hoping to find again.

I stared at the ceiling. Hoots and hollers from the "last call" crowd rang loud as they tumbled out of Daisy Buchanan's and filtered onto the street below. Outside the window, my laundry-lady neighbor retrieved a few pieces of clothes from the fire escape railing, pulled her blinds, and shut off the light.

— 24 —

After the efforts Johanna devoted to Manhattan Magic proved less than thrilling and her roommate Rachel moved in with her boyfriend, Jo faced several tough decisions. For what must've been the third instance, she brought up the option of living together in neutral territory—or "a DMZ" as she'd occasionally refer to it.

I saw an inspiring relationship in Reds—*a revolution* Johanna wrote.

This was a film she had dragged me to in the Village—it ran for over three hours and even had an intermission.

That's how it has to be for souls like you and me—the only way it can happen. . . . When John Reed said to Louise Bryant, 'Why don't we leave New York City and write what we want to write?' It made all the sense in the world to me."

Johanna had enclosed a check with her note, along with half a dozen pictures of a place upstate she'd already scoped out—a part of New York neither of us had been familiar with.

Our separations exhaust me and I would love for you to see my reality. Let's not put it off or allow money (and your pride) to stand between us . . . I'm certain it would turn out well. Though I enjoy Boston and your apartment, I also wish to share my world with you. So I'm sending you a gift and calling it a "consultation" just to make sure you'll accept it. :) The visit to Revere remains an enchanting memory . . . The walk near the water . . . was really fine . . .

So Happy Thanksgiving—would cherish the opportunity to sit in front of your Newbury Street fireplace on that day. It feels as if we met in the fall—but I know it was summer.

Call it a halfway meeting of the minds . . . at least send me your latest work . . .

Love, Johanna

On the notepaper, Jo sketched pumpkins and turkeys next to the word *Thanksgiving*. A pail and shovel along with a couple of seagulls hovered above *summer*. I tossed the check in the junk drawer of my kitchen.

Johanna told me later that because of how someone had initially described the building, she thought it might've been an abandoned train station, but discovered it was a four-bedroom house and barn instead—with close to six hundred feet of riverfront property located between the Poconos and Catskills. Johanna had learned from the real estate agent, it was *remote,* and they'd *need a car . . . Four people rented it last year, for weekends—four writers. Great vibes. Sounds like a dream . . . could be real.*

As romantic as our East Village experience had been—a period of discovery and exploration with art galleries, small theater houses, and music venues like The Bitter End all within walking distance—and, as much as I loved showing Johanna the sites of Boston as she had introduced me to New York—when obliged to return to our respective apartments, it was as if we were each forced to ride a tandem bicycle alone. What was the point of the extra seat?

I realize my reality can sometimes be rough for you, Johanna wrote in another letter. *Everything I ever wanted to be or do—my innermost self—has been interpreted by others as . . . fantasy . . . because I am un-usual and my entire life, I've tried pretending that I am ~~un~~usual,*—she'd drawn lines through the prefix—*Now that I've admitted the truth, I'm desolate. You get me . . . and our distances weigh heavily on us . . . I believe we're destined to be together—timing tells the telltale heart, what and when. What time is it, Matt?*

Still, I couldn't "pull the trigger," as Orlando was wont to say. "Put your shit in storage; take the leap. What the fuck is keeping you here?" my brother asked when I shared the news.

I couldn't come up with a suitable answer for him, Johanna, or me.

I had a nice pad, was writing for papers and journals, had been earning a few dollars, publishing essays and short stories. The night gig at Medical Records proved to be no strain and had provided me with a wonderful boss—who even let me sleep an hour or so some nights—and I'd been taking directing courses at the Loeb.

None of these facts contributed to an impassioned argument to stand pat. An inexplicable loyalty—that wasn't the correct term—an unfathomable allegiance to what, and to whom I couldn't explain, fed my hesitation.

"Do you love her?" Orlando asked.

"Of course."

Cowardice must have been the reason. Fear. Fear of leaping into unknown territory. Fear Johanna would see the real me—every frailty and flaw—and then not be intent on staying together. Fear I might discover the same in her. Fear I wouldn't be able to cut it. Fear of the impractically of it all. I'd been skirting the edges of an artistic life for years by then, while Johanna had lived and become immersed in it, earned, and scraped an existence from that choice—no matter what amount of hemorrhaging she'd suffered along the way. Was I content to remain in my comfort zone?

One summer day, you walk on a magnificent beach at dawn; white puffy clouds kiss the horizon. The sun's so bright, the wind so still, the ocean's surface presents a perfect mirror image, and the palliative seascape beckons. You're hot, sticky . . . frustrated . . . and could use—*need*—some replenishment, release, and renewal. Do you take that plunge? Strip and dive in—only to encounter an ocean floor filled with seaweed and a type of muddy quicksand that squishes between your toes and clings to your feet while you sink deeper? And, after you try to extricate your legs and lift them, shattered bottles, aluminum-can flip-tops, broken shells—what's worse, eels—target your soles while you struggle to find a secure spot to stand.

Or, do you play it safe—snap a picture, print out a couple of copies to share with a close friend or two, tell them what once was or could've been, the extent of the tale limited by your imagination?

In a scene from the movie *Frances,* the protagonist said to Harry, *You're too important to me. I'd fail you. I don't know how or why, but I would. And that's a chance I just can't take.* Strange how Johanna's hesitancy when we first met and my drive to forge a relationship appeared as though they'd been reversed.

Initially, my decision to defer Johanna's plans and leave them in a holding pattern didn't seem to be a big deal. Jo's calls became less frequent, however, and I missed those very conversations that sometimes aggravated the hell out of me. When we did speak—on the phone or in person—extended periods of silence that used to be easy turned awkward. I wondered what to make of those empty spaces stretching further and further between us and was certain Johanna did as well. Moments when Jo might've become teary-eyed in the past she now disguised, and I assumed she didn't want to look weak in my estimation or cause me to think I was obligated to *do* something.

Some higher-up at E.F. Hutton had seen and been impressed by a number of Johanna's murals displayed on the walls of a major New York bank. That a Hutton executive became aware of Jo's work at all was due to the efforts of Courtney, a member of their creative arts and advertising division, who Johanna had met after the Keller film screening. Though the style of the bank's pieces was similar to *WomenScapes* and consisted of vibrant purples and pinks placed on fabric, the subject was tamer. Still, it had been audacious for a financial institution to take that nontraditional leap of faith.

For weeks, the guy had hounded Johanna about a job at Hutton. She accepted his offer, despite the countless arguments I posed against her doing so. This seemed impulsive.

Anyone who knew Jo considered the gig at Hutton an unlikely fit for her—much more so than the faculty appointment at Phillips she'd turned down. Johanna's friends and I were in no position to question or judge. For the first time in a long while, she had been receiving a steady and significant paycheck. And, from our initial conversations, it appeared obvious her employers respected and solicited her ideas. But I believed Jo was kidding herself; it was the honeymoon period after all.

For years, the firm's slogan declared: *When E.F. Hutton Talks, People Listen.* Ubiquitous television commercials depicted men and women in churches, on airplanes—even children in kindergarten—leaning over to hear what advice Hutton's brokers offered.

Although they might've continued to heed their clients, after a few months passed, they'd stopped paying attention to Johanna and her coworkers. With each successive message from her, that evidence became apparent. She seldom called; her letters were less heartfelt and more resigned. Johanna's disappointment in me, herself, her job—what remained of her non-corporate-related art—was palpable. She fluctuated from self-denigration to blame—her target, more often than not me—once going so far as calling me "traitor" in half jest.

Johanna sent a postcard; a bilious green, ghost-like glob glared from its front. Printed beneath the creature were the words LOOK WHAT THEY'VE DONE TO MY COMPLEXION. On the flip side, she wrote:

Months here and confused why . . . People are machines . . . People are money—stocks, bonds . . . robots . . . A bizarre scene—a foreign country. I'm already looking for a way out. Bored, boring, bore, gore . . . You can bet I'm the only purple in the place, J

A callous and minuscule facet of me would've liked to dispatch a quick reply that said *Duh. . . what did you expect?"* Or *No shit, Sherlock.* My anger surprised me, and I'd dismiss those reactions almost as quickly as they'd surfaced.

The resolve with which Johanna had taken the position had shocked me and Louise. Katey, the performance artist and Jo's former business partner, also reached out in alarm. Part of Johanna's responsibilities were "to facilitate the design of welcoming spaces" for client and employee areas; but the committees, policies, and procedures she was compelled to plow through in order to accomplish anything, disconcerted her.

Please tell me what colors make up a welcome greeting? "Do certain shades and hues offend folks? Could beach and tropical island themes cause employees to become lax and not motivated to perform their jobs?"— Those are the questions that crop up and are debated ad nauseam at our meetings. And, don't get me started on the ongoing battle between traditional and abstract styles.

201

To Johanna's friends and me, it looked as though she were abandoning her craft.

"We can't get her to paint," Louise said. "Just sits and stares at a blank canvas for hours. 'What does it matter?' she'll say to me."

"Who's got energy left to create after commuting five days a week on the Metro?" I countered. Still, my unconditional defense of Johanna had wavered.

As long as I'd known Jo, these intense highs and somber lows composed an integral portion of her DNA. Truth be told, I realized why parts of her lashed out, and I sympathized. On the other hand, if not a traitor, I'd become a failed ally. And, knowing Johanna the way I believed I did, I understood on those limited occasions when she thought she'd betrayed her ideals, she would find it difficult to forgive herself.

I called to convince her to resign.

"What's the alternative?" she asked.

I fixed my eyes upon the shroud above my fireplace and, when my pause hovered in the air for one beat too many, Johanna insisted she was not the type to quit and didn't want to fail.

"Leaving Hutton would never amount to failure—in anyone's mind. You don't belong there."

"Where do I belong?" She sighed.

By that point, we'd been altering course—*drifting*, more aptly—typically communicating via postcards and letters; even those instances had dwindled. I had no intention of ending this rare phone call on a sour note.

"Get a leave of absence. Come to Boston. Live here for a while," I blurted out, to my surprise.

The silence howled.

"Johanna?"

"Life's not simply another album, Matt. You can't take a record from the sleeve and put it on the turntable again whenever you feel like it. Besides, I don't need you to be my savior."

She hung up.

With my hand still resting on the cradle, I glanced at the elaborate mirror Johanna had urged me to buy: it had performed its role too well—the room never looked larger. I wondered how many of our missteps and successes were predetermined. Did I let Jo down? Was there something more I could've done—or *should* be doing—to help? Had I been selfish?

I opened my kitchen cabinet doors, removed some dishes from the strainer, and placed them on a shelf. While rearranging the glasses, I took a few and set them on the counter—attempting to eliminate clutter. Then I went downstairs and stopped to speak to Aubrey for a few minutes.

"Hey. Just the person I'm looking for. Got the new Lionel Richie album for you."

"Huh?"

"What's wrong?"

"Nothing. A lot on my mind. . . .What album?"

"Want to talk about it? Espresso?"

"Maybe later."

Aubrey handed me a large stack of secondhand albums, along with the price gun. "$9.95," she said.

I tagged; neither of us spoke.

After she plopped a fourth pile of records in front of me, I said, "Gotta go. Sorry."

"I'm here."

Without offering Aubrey a reply, I made my way out the door.

Perfect, I thought. *Another apology due.*

I walked by a sidewalk transformer spray-painted with multi-colored graffiti. A mural of Victor Jara covered one side; handbills of all shapes and sizes plastered the other. Then I passed the happy couple from the optical shop ad. Someone had used a sharpie to draw large hoop-earrings on the girl; the guy's eyes were blackened out.

Johanna's agreeing to take the Hutton job and my not accepting her invitation to move to neutral territory would haunt us for years to come if we couldn't devise some level of accommodation. I think we both understood this; yet, we no longer shared a common language. I suggested a break for clarity's sake. But Johanna was convinced what I had been calling a very rough patch was, in reality, evidence of an alliance severed beyond salvation.

Where's your faith, young man?

. . . Why so many doubts? Timing is the essence of life and the time isn't right. It's simple. You've given up, I understand that. Call it "breathing space"—or whatever it is you said in your last letter. I realize what you're going through and don't appreciate your censorship of our friendship—you stay to yourself when you're down, while I reach out to those I love. It's a different process. I'm not afraid to show it all . . . Remember when we saw Sophie's Choice—*and* Frances? *You reminded me of the writer in both stories. You're often there for people—in most ways—not all the way, not completely. Someday you will be . . . In spite of you, I love you, J*

Months went by; I received a small packet in the mail, slit an end open, and flicked it over. Out popped the keys I'd given Jo two years before. I

205

rubbed the raised surface of the silver Saint Joanna key chain I bought the night we stopped at Copley Flair, dropped it into a kitchen drawer, and spied the uncashed check Johanna had sent me. I stepped on the pedal of my trash bin; the cover flipped, and I tossed the empty envelope in. A faint scent of peach shampoo was all that remained.

When I was younger, around the time my cousin Vinnie was preparing to get shipped off to Khe Sanh, he, Brother Bruce, and I had kicked a high-end Adidas soccer ball all over the church parking lot. After building up a sweat, Brother finally removed his perspiration-drenched t-shirt along with his Saint Anthony necklace. Taken aback—I'd never seen him without that medal, even during legitimate basketball, football, and soccer games.

So I asked about it. "God doesn't care what you're wearing, Matt. It's inside that counts," he said.

Vinnie smirked. "If he only knew what was going on in *my* insides."

A few days later, my cousin gave me that soccer ball.

I played with it for the rest of the season. It helped keep me in shape until the day it abruptly rolled off the tips of my fingers at Short Beach, bounced on rocks and sand to the shoreline, and was carried out by the tide. The ball flowed back in my direction and teased me for a few moments, riding atop an incoming wave or two—before drifting away.

— 26 —

It was Louise who called me. Louise who found Johanna and afterwards cleaned up the remnants of Jo's vomit from a throw rug we once bought for a lark simply because it had cow faces on it. And Louise who scrubbed blood from the sofa cushion where it had spilled after the EMTs' first IV attempt failed.

I had to figure out the fastest way to get there. Despite my fears, the only option was to take a plane. Considering the many concerts I'd covered, my trips to New York and to places much further, it was astounding I'd been able to avoid confronting my fear of flying for that long. I *had* phoned Amtrak earlier in the day; waited on hold for close to forty-five minutes, then caved.

When I sought Orlando's advice, he contacted Eastern Airlines, purchased a ticket, and even offered to drive me to Logan.

During the ride—besides giving me a pep talk— he delivered a few air travel pointers.

"At takeoff, the centrifugal force thrusts you

against your seat. It's like nothing you've experienced before."

"Great."

"Think of the old Tilt-A-Whirl at the beach—only on steroids."

Already more than nauseous, I was devastated about Johanna—and we hadn't reached the airport yet.

In full-on instructor mode, my brother said, "And they'll give you this preflight lesson outlining the proper procedure for putting on facemasks when they drop from ceiling compartments in event of an emergency. And how chair cushions can be used as flotation devices—yeah, as if that could ever happen. Forget about it—no fuckin' airline veteran pays attention to one bit of those drills. Anyone who catches you watching will guess you're green and afraid."

And what would be wrong with that? I should have asked. But understanding the Revere code of our youth, I knew enough to keep my mouth shut.

I was indebted to Orlando for getting me a spot near the window. "Listen. You don't have to look out. I understand. Who's gonna know? Though it's kind of special to watch streaming headlights and city sparkles at night. And you'll want that seat anyway—for privacy, if nothing else."

I couldn't decide where to place my sweaty palms during the car ride—resting them first on Orlando's dashboard. When he appeared to interpret the maneuver as a criticism of his driving skills, I rubbed them on my jeans, put them on the door handle, and back on top of my knees. Most of this apprehension was reserved for Johanna, and not the upcoming flight.

My brother carried my bag to the gate, gave me a hug and a kiss on the cheek before walking away. Then he turned around, hugged me again. "You *are* a good person. You realize that, don't you?"

I couldn't imagine Orlando detected something solely by looking at me, but couldn't fathom how he picked up on my remorse. And it hadn't been because of anything I'd let slip, because I'd hardly spoken a word during our fifteen-minute drive.

"I wasn't supposed to be home that early," Louise said in the cab ride we shared to the hospital. "I'd arranged to meet Rachel, our old roommate, for dinner after work. She came down with a bad cold and fever, so canceled."

We passed Tompkins Square Park, the Surf Maid, Bleecker Street Cinema, and The Bottom Line along the way.

The little I'd heard regarding suicide attempts until that point was what I guessed most everyone had been told: it was often a cry for help. Some therapists and doctors assert many people—even the incredibly lonely and isolated—have no intention of following through with the act. That several "stage" (not my term—from some article) their efforts in such a manner they're fairly certain a friend or family member will be close by to intervene. Supposedly that was in the mind of writer Sylvia Plath—same magazine piece.

Who conducted this type of post "episode" research? And how could anyone know for sure?

When I learned Louise had planned to be at a restaurant with Rachel for a few hours or longer, I came to the conclusion Johanna must've opted for a measure more significant than a plea for help.

In awe of Jo's strength since forever, I couldn't make sense of what she'd done. From the outside looking in, I'd always considered suicide a selfish act. Until it happened to someone I loved. Then all bets—as well as judgments—were off. Strange how that worked. Johanna was a lot of things. I'd witnessed her being short-tempered, insecure, passionate, stubborn—and even petty. Selfishness had never been a weapon in her arsenal. Envy was another trait I'd never seen her exhibit.

How Jo ended up on the floor was anybody's guess. Occasionally, she'd display a flair for the dramatic in front of me, but would've been loath to have spectators partake in that sort of melodrama. Knowing Louise would need to clean up after her would've mortified Jo as well; it may sound ludicrous, but she was too proud for that. I tried not to dwell on the why and the wherefore, partly because it was morbid and I preferred to focus on the Johanna I believed I'd known. And mostly because I understood the search for these answers could be a fool's errand destined to occupy a person's thoughts for years. Recognizing this was not the same as calling off the quest.

I asked Louise if Johanna had left a note.

She hunched forward, drummed her fingers on the protective Plexiglas covering the picture and license number of our cab driver, then shook her head no before adding, "Not really."

We turned around the hospital corridor; I was startled to find Ted in Johanna's room.

"Sorry," Louise whispered. "With everything going on, I forget to tell you."

At least here he wouldn't have the opportunity to discuss his favorite new bass solo.

Ted nodded, then backed out to allow Louise and me to enter.

Closed and lightly bruised, I imagined it would be an effort for Johanna to open her lids. Her body limp, she looked like one of those dolls whose eyes shut as soon as you tip their head back. I wanted to ease Jo forward, so she'd wake from this nightmare—and so I'd be able to as well.

She attempted to smile.

Louise said, "That's OK. You don't have to talk, Jo. We're not staying long."

Johanna opened her eyes briefly and shut them again. We sat on guest chairs lining the wall. After a few moments, Louise left us alone. I edged closer to the bed and placed my hand in Jo's.

"Hey." She tried to force a grin.

"Hey."

For the next twenty minutes, medical machines chimed and beeped in a cacophonic symphony. Some chants came from Johanna's room, while others contributed a background chorus from the adjoining one and beyond. The barely audible sounds of Pavarotti could be heard from the nurse's station. He sang "Nessun Dorma" which segued into "O Sole Mio." Someone must have compiled a mix tape—the best of PBS Masterpiece, Time-Life Presents, or a similar col-

213

lection. Though I appreciated the irony in both songs and accepted that the gods were content to mock me, I didn't mind listening. I held Johanna's hand tight. A poor imitation of Cezanne's *Apples and Pears* hung on the wall, and I wasn't certain if Johanna could see this impressionist wannabe in her current state. She would've despised the piece. "Hospital-issued gluck" she might've labeled it.

I kissed Jo on the forehead and gently drew my hand away; she woke and grasped it. "Sorry" was all she could manage.

"Me too."

I kissed her again, then walked out.

"Mild bipolar disorder," Louise said to me after we returned to the apartment. "That's their so-called *qualified* diagnosis, at this point."

"Mild." Johanna would've ridiculed that aspect of their assessment—there was nothing "mild" about anything she did. Jo was all in, or not at all. The diagnosis akin to a doctor telling a patient she had a mild form of cancer.

"What's the qualified part mean?"

"I guess Jo's displayed many of the identified symptoms; they're not entirely sure."

It turned out Johanna had confessed to Louise

she'd been prescribed meds as far back as time spent in Wisconsin. But the side effects caused her arms to jerk involuntarily as well as other tics, and this was a problem during interviews and presentations—not to mention when she painted. Jo's arm sometimes behaved like a felled telephone pole after it had crashed to the ground in the middle of a storm. And, when that occurred, Johanna's brain could no longer communicate with her hand because "the wires got disconnected."

Louise gave me a sad smile. "And besides, Jo said she'd been feeling so much better once she met you."

After a while, Louise let me know Ted had been in the picture for several months.

"She was treading water, floundering, you know? And she hated herself for picking back up with him—Jo took it as a telltale sign of weakness. But he kept hovering round. A fuckin' gnat—in my mind, anyway. Johanna might've viewed things differently. His band-mates went their separate ways, and he fawned over her. I figured there might be some ulterior motive; though he did help in a few respects. And Jo believed you'd given up on your relationship . . . on her."

Louise's gaze softened. "Sorry. I didn't mean that the way it came out."

But, I understood; she was only delivering a statement of fact—a single line for the case file, an entry on my rap sheet.

"That night, I hadn't expected to find Johanna here. She'd been staying at Ted's place for a few weeks."

Louise told me she'd changed the sheets and I should sleep in Johanna's room. We drew closer to kiss good night; both of us lingered longer than we should have. My hands massaged her shoulders, then caressed her butt. I leaned in for a second kiss before spying an orphaned plant of Jo's standing guard at a bay window and edging a few steps back.

Louise tore her hands from my waist as if they'd suddenly been struck by static electricity. She placed one behind her neck, and adjusted the leaves of a hanging ivy with the other.

I rationalized our impulses. "Rough day."

"Yeah."

Guilty eyes locked; I turned first and walked into Johanna's bedroom. The Sadat bubblehead—sitting silent and still on an end table beneath the *Missing Jack & Ace painting*—glared. I grabbed the bedspread, headed for the alcove, and fell onto the sofa bed— without fussing to open it.

Alone the next day, I visited Johanna. Exhausted and on heavy meds, she searched deliberately for each word—as an elderly person might shift his or her foot on a sleet-covered sidewalk for a dry spot to anchor. I'd been praying that some non-verbal forms of communication we'd cultivated in the early days would return. But months had now passed and while we were still connected, we weren't in sync. Though not awkward, it was . . . different.

To combat Jo's incredible thirst, I filled plastic cups with ice chips and cold water repeatedly. Whenever she woke, I held them up to her lips so she could drink from a straw.

"Pour some for the baby," she said a couple of times. When I asked what she meant, she'd stare at me, then lie down and fall asleep. Blood stains dappled the dressing that kept her IV in place.

I read from a book I'd taken for the plane ride. The hardcover version of *Candide* was inscribed *To the Skeptic . . . Love, the Believer.* When a nurse checked in, I learned Johanna was scheduled to stay in a rehab facility for three weeks or more after discharge.

Ted showed up around four; I excused myself and left.

On the cab trip back, I had the driver drop me off

at Washington Square Park and walked the remaining blocks to East Seventh and Avenue B.

"Thank God for E.F. Hutton," I said to Louise that night, hoping to inject a touch of gallows humor.

"Why?"

"The place that helped put Jo in the hospital is now providing her with decent medical coverage. The first time she's had insurance since married to that dentist years ago."

Louise didn't smile.

Before returning to Boston, I connected with my sister. Francesca had a production of *Cinderella* being staged in town, and it made sense to meet for lunch.

Our reconciliation was long overdue. But the last few times I'd seen her, Franny had been pissed off or still appeared to be carrying a level of disappointment about our parents' behavior and an upbringing neither of us could've changed. I guess I'd understood this early on or had tried to ignore the nagging questions she couldn't let go. The ensuing drama had grown too much for me.

Five years older than me, humor had never been one of Francesca's strong points while growing up. That talent was Orlando's domain. So it had struck me as more than ironic when I read a review of *Cinderella* that called her efforts "amusing"—and intentionally so. Not that Franny didn't have more than a few reasons to be irate—especially after the way my mother and father treated her when she confessed to them she was in love and the object of her affection was her best friend Melody.

Not an earth-shattering revelation in my mind, and it had thrilled me because they were happy. Shouldn't that important piece of the puzzle have been enough for Mom and Dad? It wasn't asking a great deal. Before he died, my father came around. For our mother, though, acceptance took longer. By the time she'd recognized her mistakes, Franny had already graduated from college. Ashamed of her conduct, I suppose Ma thought it too late—or not possible—to make any serious attempt to repair the damage and Francesca had little tolerance for her by then.

"Please come to the show tonight. You can crash at our place," Franny said before we had an opportunity to be seated.

"Have to catch the train. Sorry. Next visit, I promise."

I regretted this too-swift response the moment I heard it escape my lips; I hadn't even given my sister's invitation a moment's consideration. "Promise," I repeated—hoping we wouldn't fall back into our assigned roles—then reached out and patted the top of her hand.

I decided not to share many details about Johanna. Orlando and Franny kept in touch; though I wasn't certain how often that was. But, after having not been in my sister's company for such a long time, I *knew* I had no desire to get into it with her. I only told Franny I was in the city to see friends and hinted at hardly anything else.

She loved me as I did her; nonetheless, when my sister lapsed into the role of therapist or counselor, those sessions elicited the opposite effect I believed she intended and I ended up feeling uneasy.

"You OK?" she said more than once.

"Fine. You should try to see Mom. She's always asking about you guys."

"Me and *Melody*? Or only me?"

"You guys. *Guys* . . . gals—you two . . . whatever . . ."

"Well. Maybe—you sure you're alright?"

Giving me no chance to respond, she said, "Ma and Dad should've done better by you. Should have gotten you help—and some for themselves while they were at it. Matt, you *know* that, don't you?"

"Don't start. Do we have to go there? Again? They could only parent with the skills they had."

After we finished our meals and some coffee, I signaled for the waitress. I insisted on paying the check—even though I had a good idea my big sister earned a decent living. I had a flashback to the dinner Franny and I shared when we were kids in New York City decades before. But on this particular day, I'd barely noticed what our server looked like.

It might have been easier for me to forgive our parents. I'm not convinced. Either way, I faced a situation over which I had minimal control.

Louise promised she'd leave work early and walk with me to the subway station. I assured her that while I appreciated the gesture, it wasn't necessary. She persisted.

When we got to West 4th Street, Louise handed me a navy blue envelope.

"What's this?"

"Something I should've given you before. Read it on the ride home."

I unzipped my carryon bag and put it inside the copy of *Candide*.

An hour into the journey, I opened the envelope. A post-it stuck to Johanna's handwritten note read *Matt, Found this on Jo's bedside table that night.*

A letter composed in two parts, the first dated six months prior, said:

Dearest Matt:

It's Friday. I'm blue as this paper. When does the pain end? I feel like letting go, letting the rage out . . . Afraid to call you. Not sure why? . . . There's an element in you I'm frightened to look at. Genuine love? I can't believe it's true . . . It's not in my vocabulary—not with men, anyway . . .

I'm scared and not worthy . . . The river is wide—I need to cross over. But don't remember how to swim. Have to break away from NYC. It's killing my spirit. I don't want to live on the dark side of the moon anymore. . . the question is: where? You can't go home again—don't know where home is. Last month, Louise hired a fortune teller for us as a lark—Tarot cards, the whole deal . . . and she said she couldn't find one root on me . . . What does that mean? That I'm not a plant—I'm not growing?

Think about me. I'm not who you perceive me to be. Try to see the real me . . . not just a fantasy. My realities—though not pleasant—are part of me. . . . I might have said this before, when I saw Frances, *you were Harry . . . in* Sophie's Choice, *you were the young writer. I was the woman in both those movies, and I'm not necessarily proud of it . . . promise you'll be my friend to the end—I swear I will, Johanna*

The next section, written in different color ink, was dated a few days before Jo wound up in the hospital:

Here everything is so concentrated and impossible to hide. That's what I'm fighting now—the verge/urge? To get away. The ultimate escape, instead of throwing myself in deeper. Why have I become such a coward? Or am I? Is it wisdom? Fatigue? Or both? I have more questions than answers these days. My life is flashing before me and I'm not doing enough. . . . it's not cosmic . . . I detest the mundane practicalities and I hate the fact my handwriting is going to shit/hell too :) . . . Sometimes I realize I AM too much—too intense—too serious. You brought out the humor in me, which~~makes~~ made it easier to laugh at myself and the little idiosyncrasies we all have . . . I hope to make my contribution before it's too late . . .

— 28 —

Some weekends, I'd hop on the Green Line to the Blue out to my mother's house for an "authentic" meal—as she called it. On the return trip to my apartment, I'd be bogged down with care packages of vinegar peppers, breaded cutlets, meatballs soaked in tomato sauce, and an assortment of cold cuts. A tough gig, but somebody had to do it. Many of these staples Ma prepared on the day of the visit, while other provisions got delivered from Ferrante's, a local market, if she had received advance notice from me.

A classic stereotype to be sure, most Italians I knew growing up believed food could provide sustenance for any form of hunger and not simply that related to diet. This didn't always pan out; from time to time however, the meals and associated camaraderie kept a few wolves at bay.

Usually I'd schedule these visits as a diversion or

because I hadn't seen Mom in a while. On that occasion, it had been an absolute necessity. I couldn't sit in my empty apartment one more hour and be cross-examined by Johanna's artwork, or the handwritten scraps of notes she'd taped on door frames, cabinets, or even my coffee cup—messages I'd left hanging all those months later: *Downstairs doing laundry, At Deluca's for wine, Heat plate in toaster oven for 5 to 6 minutes—NO LESS!, Meeting Beth for lunch, I miss you MORE.*

And there were only so many browsing trips I could take to nearby book or record stores and not have them remind me of a favorite singer or author of Johanna's, some other aspect of her—or of us.

One day Aubrey helped lift the gloom with an invitation to a Debbie Gibson concert courtesy of some tickets the Atlantic Records rep had given her. Aubrey once teased me unmercifully when she spotted me tapping my foot and grooving to "Out of the Blue" in her store—I'd been a closet "Debhead" before the phrase had been coined. But Aubrey, the dyed-in-the-wool punk rock aficionado, surprised me by admitting to being a fan of sixties bubblegum music—1910 Fruitgum Company, The Archies, and the like—and told me she found Gibson's tunes in that vein. I was disappointed when I met up with her at the venue and, rather than just the two of us, we were joined by four of Aubrey's other buddies. Several times that night, when she caught me gazing down our row, past those friends—at her and not the stage—she'd wink. Instead of returning the gesture, I'd look away, embarrassed.

"Johanna's such a talented artist—your father would've enjoyed getting to know her," Mom said, and she couldn't stray from the "What a nice girl" and "When will *we* see her again?" mantras during that visit. Orlando had respected my wishes and shared nothing concerning Johanna's condition with Mom. I appreciated that—although he might've had his own reasons.

An initial evasive maneuver that sprung to my mind was the marvelously creative "She's been busy at work" followed up with "We're taking a break for a while." I couldn't imagine my mother's reaction if we endeavored to discuss Johanna's depression like a couple of proper adults.

"What did *you* do now?" she challenged.

I did my best to convince her I had not done a thing wrong—knowing that wasn't quite true—and I still loved Johanna.

She advised me to "give it time"—her answer for

most everything as long as I'd lived. *Your dad will come around; give it time. You'll grow to love spaghetti with clam sauce; give it time.* And—for most of my teenage existence—*Give it time; you'll feel better soon.*

Though patience *could* be a virtue, I'd also learned—the hard way—that inactivity could be a vice.

While I was in the Village, Louise had divulged history of Johanna I hadn't been privy to. "She had a late-term miscarriage. Only a few weeks before her due date, her husband got them into a nasty car accident. He'd been drunk."

I'd picked up the watering can from an end table, walked to a window, and tended to Jo's plants.

Louise's revelation shed light on an allusion Johanna made to "the baby" at the hospital. I'd been puzzled by her comments of course, but wondered if it had been the "meds talking." She'd been drifting in and out, speaking fragments of ragtime during her first few days there yet—even if Johanna were entirely lucid—that would not have been the moment to ask her what she meant.

I'd looked out through the clear glass pane but saw nothing; it wasn't until Louise jerked the can out of my hands that I'd heard water dripping from the planter and onto their hardwood floor.

"Johanna lost a son," Louise said. "She told me things weren't good between them anyway—dismal, from the sounds of it. Getting pregnant might have been their attempt to save the marriage. She gave up blaming him after a while and knew she had to make a clean break."

I sent flowers to Jo at the rehab. Louise would call me—or I her—for updates on Johanna's status as well as her own. Though Louise and I had drawn closer, we never mentioned our embrace that night in the apartment.

Besides my ongoing discussions with Louise, I tried calling Johanna more than a few times, until the night she greeted me with one of the saddest sentences in the English language: "I can't talk now; I'm not alone."

On the rare occasions when we did connect, those conversations were *polite*—another distasteful term— with neither Johanna nor I capable of finding our way back to the theme of *us.* So, we skirted around it by dancing the weather-report waltz or discussing a recent gallery exhibit. These exchanges brought to mind a concert Johanna and I once attended at Boston's Symphony Hall. Only now it was as if it were the next day and a different performance. Though the orchestra played a familiar Rachmaninoff concerto, several wrong notes marred the event. And, as the musicians struggled to get on key, we longed for the strains we'd remembered hearing the previous evening.

Soon, Johanna and I stopped these recitals and our phone calls ceased.

Jo continued to send an occasional note or postcard. In one, she shared news of a doctor she was enthusiastic about, a person who had more than a cursory understanding of art as well as psychiatry and had prescribed a "mix"—as Johanna called it—of medications that had so far lessened, or even removed, many earlier side effects. This new physician didn't believe she'd been suffering from bipolar disease; rather, it might've been a condition known as PMDD, or premenstrual dysphoric disorder. Jo informed me there'd been insufficient research performed on it though, and they had asked her to take part in a clinical trial.

A few months later, she wrote:

Decided to pull it together—explore the Left coast, see what there is to offer. NYC should remain what it is—a nice place to visit, but you wouldn't want to live there. :(I need to purify myself. Parts of me died here. And, it's time to revive before it becomes a cancer. You understand sides of me no one knows—that's why we should never try to define or qualify what we have. . . . You are—and always will be—very dear and special, regardless of how things work out in the long run. . . . I hope we meet again . . . Once in a while, I look back on that Andover job—and think how easy it would have been.

Maybe that's why I said no—a tough decision—like refusing a delicious piece of cheesecake. Regrets are not my style . . .

I clung to a smidgeon of optimism: Johanna had used the present tense—"what we *have.*" Perhaps we could end up similar to those entwined birch trees in Appleton Jo sometimes painted? Still, being referred to as "special" hadn't thrilled me, and I recognized I'd been kidding myself.

Early on, Johanna's dad urged her to separate those birches. "Pick one. And yank the other from the ground—roots and all. Otherwise they'll both die." But she couldn't do it, having already become the willful gardener by then.

"Somehow they survived, sharing that same plot of land," Jo told me. "Those trees kept spiraling until they mingled at their crowns. I could never tell whose leaves were whose."

231

I thought of one of our last good afternoons to-gether—Johanna and I managed to cuddle on that tiny $99 bargain during a frosty winter spell—and then a number of other "Best Of" days. It turned out that most of those had been spur of the moment with no preconceived master plan. We'd read books and share select passages from each. Later, while sitting on the floor—my record collection sprawled every-where—Johanna would surprise me with her eclectic musical tastes. Several of her favorite artists: Jett, Geils, Van Morrison, Rickie Lee—and, of course, Dylan—overlapping with mine. And Jo being as en-thused as me after I'd found a mono version of an album—*Blonde on Blonde*—and both of us discovered the prominence of different instruments when com-pared to the stereo edition. Johanna could barely car-ry a tune. That didn't stifle her enthusiasm, and she did her utmost when singing "One of Us Must Know" and other songs from that double LP, and I loved her for it. Afterwards, we'd watch movies and though her preferences never strayed much from In-die stuff, she'd readily indulge my growing but alarming tendency towards sappy romance.

I'd look at the plants that hugged the Newbury Street fireplace and think of my life before Johanna, when it wouldn't have been possible for me to keep a plastic flower alive. During each successive stopover in Boston, Jo would head out for a walk by herself and return with another potted mystery along with specific suggestions: *This gal craves lots of sun. Hydrate. Don't forget; feed the Ficus with a tablespoon of that mix on the mantle.*

"Comfortable" wasn't the correct term. "Contented" or "at ease" made us sound like old fogies. But with Johanna—in between her roller coaster detours—I *had* encountered a type of stillness, a serenity I guess I hadn't known I was capable of, and if I ever had been, it had been too long ago to remember.

— 29 —

When Johanna sent me a note several months later to let me know she was pregnant, Ted had been offered an A & R job at a record label in Arizona, and she was in line for an adjunct teaching position at a university there, it wasn't a big surprise.

After what Louise had shared with me about Johanna losing the baby many years before, it made sense she would try to seek the kind of comfortable living most folks dreamed of and one I'd always wished for her. In college, Professor Garber had discussed Shakespeare's liminal characters, and Puck from *Midsummer Night's Dream* now came to mind. It was past time for me to cross the threshold. Besides, when would Dear Abby suggest the proper moment was to back away after the woman you'd been desperately in love with told you she was carrying another man's child?

We'd performed our compulsory but civil breakup scene after most of the blame, as well as the subtle—and not-so-subtle—digs had been dispensed. This happened in Tompkins Square Park, of all places. Women pushed strollers, while people hustled to work or lunch breaks. Sitting together on a patch of grass between an elm and pear tree, clear sky overhead—no overlapping leaf canopies in sight—we promised to keep in touch.

A small rubber ball rolled towards us; I kneeled and stretched to reach it. When I looked up, a girl—about three or four years old—had her arms outspread. I lobbed the ball, and she caught it with one hand.

"Great catch."

She smiled timidly before heading in the direction of her mother, who mouthed the words "Thank you."

The kid hugged her mom, then Johanna sighed before gazing skyward. "It's getting late."

She stared at the clouds as though they housed a clock face.

Yet, days, weeks—even months—later, a part of me still considered Johanna a damsel in distress—no matter how many examples of her resiliency and courage I'd witnessed in the past. As certain as I was that when the going got tough, Ted would bail once again, I owed Jo this opportunity. The right thing to do was to offer my best wishes and move on. It wasn't as if I had any other choice; most of the decision-making had been taken out of my hands long before Johanna ended up in that hospital bed in New York City.

Aubrey

— 30 —

One evening, I stopped by 33 1/3. Guns N' Roses and Aerosmith posters had replaced Michael Jackson's. An extremely large ad with the cover of Debbie Gibson's *Anything Is Possible* album hung on the wall behind the front counter. Aubrey had scrawled *I love you Matt, Deb* at the bottom, and I caught her handiwork for the first time.

"Very funny."

Maybe it was my overall morose attitude or the fact that when she thrust a Dead Kennedys record into my hands I didn't protest, but Aubrey sensed something was amiss and cajoled me into taking her up on her long-standing offer to have a drink at Daisy Buchanan's. Dressed in a light-gray softball jersey with *The Phoenix* printed on the back and matching sweats, black stripes—the type that ball players rub on to cut down on the sun's glare—bordered the tops of her cheeks.

"We had a game before my shift started. I gotta change before we go out."

"You look fine—*hot*, actually."

"Too bad," she teased. "I wanted our first official date to be special."

Our dance of flirtation had been ongoing for months and hadn't waned, yet Aubrey flirted with a variety of folks who frequented the store—guys and gals: aspiring stand-up comics, band members, readers of her column—and not only geeky fans of singer-songwriters. If there was anything more than that between us, I'd missed the signs.

We snagged one of Daisy's rare tables among its barstools and sat in a corner. Even though the place didn't feature disco—there had never been enough room—a DJ spun records in a cordoned-off section close to the entrance. Content instead to watch Aubrey smile, I paid no attention to what songs he played. We ordered beers and burgers; I toyed with a plastic ketchup dispenser while we waited for our food. Two or three guys wearing uniforms akin to Aubrey's sauntered by to chat with her. One even rested his butt on the edge of our table. They spoke about a great catch she'd made at third base that afternoon—stopping a would-be winning run from scoring. I found it difficult to believe it was only that potential score and her abilities on the diamond they were interested in. Grateful the meal arrived and interrupted this banter, I asked for another round.

Aubrey watched the guys walk away and I couldn't figure out if she was being her charming self or if an element of coquettishness was in play.

"I could be satisfied eating the bacon and buns without the meat," she said.

Taking that as my cue, I grinned, pried two crispy slices from my burger, and placed them on the side of her plate.

"My hero."

She removed pickles from her sandwich.

"Didn't you order it with them?"

"I did. But aren't there times when you simply want to savor a trace of something—rather than the entire package?"

Perspiration caused my legs to stick to the seat covering, and the red vinyl snapped whenever I adjusted myself. It hadn't helped I'd forgotten the pub didn't take credit cards, and I was forced to ask Aubrey to loan me money. But she knew the bartender on duty and waltzed over to him. He clicked open the ancient, non-electric cash register with two fingers and slipped what I assumed was an IOU tab under its drawer.

Before Aubrey sat back down, she leaned against the brick wall and an ivy-covered mini bulb set strung across the ceiling seemed to frame her head. She sparkled like those women you'd see dancing in Renaissance Faires who donned crowns of real flowers and glowed with a light all their own.

After dinner, Aubrey suggested tequila shots. I glanced at the jocks who came by earlier—and had been looking in our direction a good percentage of the night—and reluctantly agreed.

Later, we shepherded each other up the stairs and staggered into my apartment before falling onto the bed.

Stretched and bent so uncomfortably tight against the fabric of my briefs that I was certain to cause permanent harm and jeopardize my ability to procreate, I reached down clumsily to unzip my pants with one hand and kept the other cradled beneath Aubrey's neck so our kissing could continue unabated. When my fumbling took too long in her estimation, she ripped off my jeans and the rest of my clothes.

Aubrey placed her finger to my lips; I parted them and licked it. She ran its moist tip along my chin, down my neck and chest, until she stopped and teased a circle around my lower belly. Finally, she worked her way further south to caress and tug. Aubrey acted as if she'd discovered a newfound toy that was hers alone. She smiled licentiously and grabbed tighter. I fiddled with the remaining buttons of her half-opened, grass-stained softball jersey—snapping one or two—before I buried my face between her breasts.

Aubrey climbed on top. Patient, in no hurry, she clearly intended us to experience the delights of this ride.

I woke after a few hours, somewhat disoriented. You could've classified what happened as a mercy fuck, I guess—at least that had been the expression at the time. I'd always despised the term. Not because I was too proud to be the recipient of a woman's benevolence—I just needed Aubrey's and my passion to be something else instead. That I couldn't stop dwelling on the whys and wherefores disturbed me.

Aubrey and I had known each other a long time by then—we cared for one another. Was it necessary for me to attach a label to everything? Or had I been assuaging guilt? The image of John Lennon from Johanna's old postcard stared at me from his perch on my bedroom mirror. I hadn't heard from her in over three months, and more than a year had passed since we'd seen each other face to face.

Second-guessing was not a practice Aubrey appeared to obsess about. I could picture her offering advice in her column by paraphrasing Gordon Gekko from the movie *Wall Street;* only she would've substituted the word "greed" with "sex":

The point is, ladies and gentleman, that sex is good. Sex is right. Sex works. Sex clarifies, cuts through, and captures the essence of the evolutionary spirit. Sex—in all of its forms—has marked the upward surge of humankind.

Hard again, I rubbed Aubrey's back, but she was still out cold. So I turned on my side, did my best to ignore my erection, and struggled to fall asleep.

At nearly 3 a.m., Aubrey nudged my shoulder to rouse me. She was holding a tray with snacks from what remained of a care package from my mom.

"Surprised you could rummage up that stuff," I said.

She handed me a beer.

"Thanks for slumming tonight." I tipped the bottle in her direction as a salute, then swigged.

"Fuck off."

Way to go, Matt.

"You suppose I sleep with just anyone? Well, fuck bloody off. I wanted to be with you. *Want* to. And I'm disappointed you'd think otherwise."

I couldn't figure out how or why a British idiom had unexpectedly found its way into Aubrey's speech.

She put on her sweatpants and stumbled on one leg before she could pull them up. Aubrey gathered her jersey, bra, and panties, clutched them against her breasts, and headed for the door.

I tried to leap out of bed to stop her; my feet tangled in the covers, and I tripped and fell forward. My left eye just missed one of those nicely trimmed—or were they *turned*?—spindles Orlando had fixed to the corners before my face smacked onto a new linoleum tile he'd recently installed.

"I'm sorry." I peered at Aubrey from the floor. "Really sorry."

I stood up, held my eye, which had taken the brunt of the fall, and walked towards her. With my free hand, I clung to Aubrey's shoulder, bent to kiss her, and she shoved me. Her clothes tumbled in a heap.

"Screw you," she said—her cadence still clipped, but with less venom.

Aubrey snatched the blanket, wrapped it around

245

the exposed top half of her body, strode into the living room and plopped onto the Bob's Discount special I'd yet to dispose of.

I grabbed an icepack before joining her on the far end of the sofa. Sounding remarkably similar to Johanna that night we first slept together in the East Village, I told Aubrey all the reasons she shouldn't be with me: my baggage, moods—an entire litany. As if I'd hoped to sabotage any chance we might've had before the relationship began. If I couldn't get a grip soon, it wouldn't take a tea leaf reader—or the *Numerology and The Divine Triangle* book Johanna once gave me—to predict my ultimate destiny: a desperate, single, mid-30s guy, eating alone at Daisy's, corner booth.

The only thing left to do about my breakup with Johanna was to clean up like a member of the New York City highway crew following a Macy's Thanksgiving Day parade. Sure, there had been several colorful floats, bright music, and gigantic helium-filled Disney-character balloons—even a visit from Santa. But the once-glittering confetti—now stained and soiled—along with empty plastic cups and Popsicle sticks were all that survived. It would be dark shortly. *Jesus, Matt, go home already.*

For the next few hours, Aubrey and I sat on that

uncomfortable sofa bed watching an interminable version of *War and Peace* starring Audrey Hepburn on Channel 4. As the room grew colder and the night wore on, Aubrey begrudgingly edged closer to me. Though I sought to elevate this low level cuddling to actions that might more fittingly be termed huddling, she'd have none of it.

By 5:30 a.m., Napoleon found his Waterloo, light filtered through my grate-shielded windows, and Aubrey had fallen asleep.

I tucked a Gloucester fisherman throw pillow—another Bob's discovery—under Aubrey's head, dug out a comforter from the closet, covered her, and retreated to the bedroom.

I woke to Aubrey sleeping beside me and wasn't certain when she crawled back in. Rather than declaring a victory, I deduced the discomfort of the sofa and the early morning chill had driven her return. I caressed Aubrey's hair, and when her deep brown eyes flickered open, she let me continue.

Later, Aubrey made coffee and toasted some bagels for us. Naked from the waist up, she brought the food.

"How d'you get like this?" I asked.

"Like what?"

"I don't know. So frank. So honest?"

247

I also thought—and wanted to say—*so in your face,* but hesitated and kept silent, mindful of her nearby cup of hot coffee.

"Therapy, my dear Watson. Therapy." Aubrey smiled, which accentuated the dimples on her cheeks.

The skeptic in me resurfaced. I envied those folks who claimed they could flush their mind of its clutter, rid themselves of oppressive thoughts, as if simply taking an eraser to a blackboard on the last day of school before summer break began. What I'd give to be half as free as Aubrey appeared to be—without the inhibitions that labored overtime. *At what cost that freedom?* I wondered.

Aubrey told me about her abusive stepdad; it hadn't been sexual, thank God, but encompassed nearly everything else I could imagine.

"After he hooked up with my mother, before long he'd tell me I was no good—wouldn't amount to anything. Some days, he'd lock me in a small pantry off of our kitchen when Mom went to work. Ridicule me. And the times I complained to her about it, she'd barely listen. Didn't believe me. I lived on the streets for a while before an aunt took me in."

I'm not sure what triggered it that day, that morning, that hour. Perhaps Franny's oft-repeated idea that I needed more support as a kid, or the sleep-deprived and hangover-filled long day's journey into night I was spending with the graciously generous Aubrey, maybe the daybreak java that had segued into countless bloody Marys—after the short hop we made downstairs to Deluca's—or it could've been the uncanny way in which Aubrey reminded me of Heather, which I'd yet to put my finger on, or because of the combination of all these factors that had miraculously aligned but, I somehow found the strength to share with her the story of Heather and Scott, my childhood friends from Revere.

— 31 —

After discarding her customary tomboy attire and stepping into a gown from Franny's university theater production, my sister revealed how transfixed Heather had become. With a change of scenery, different garb, and an older woman to confide in, Heather bonded with Francesca.

Following that long-ago afternoon, I'd kept my promise to Heather and shared nothing with our gang about her wearing makeup and a dress. This led to a kind of implicit truce going forward. Heather—still annoying as hell—continued to insist she could do anything we guys could. When we protested—as we had on the baseball diamond—she would somehow prove us wrong. Whether it be diving off "the curve"—a jagged portion of cement that jutted out from the rest of the seawall—and landing among large boulders in less than ten feet of water where, legend had it, someone from our parents' generation once severed his spinal cord, or showing us up once more by climbing trees and reaching spots higher than anybody could.

"It's because she's so skinny," I'd say—she couldn't have been more than sixty-five or seventy pounds. Heather was fearless; heights didn't faze her—little seemed to. She was the first to enter old Apply's farm one Halloween. The homestead had been abandoned for years, its windows decrepit and boarded up, its floors weak and creaky. I doubt anyone believed those ridiculous ghost legends; however, we had seen and heard the screeching bats, fallen timber, and clusters of rats. Even Damian lined up behind Heather that night and refused to go in before she did.

In her senior year, Franny had been coming home from college less and less, but one weekend, a few months after the day in front of the dresser, Heather came by and asked to speak with her.

From what Franny would share with me later, one of Heather's mother's visitors—Papa Logan, Daddy Bill, Uncle Ryan, or some other stupid "friend"—had snuck into Heather's bedroom, pulled down the covers, forced a kiss on her and put his hands under her pajama bottoms. Heather escaped his grasp by pretending to be sick long enough to run to another room, lock the door, and—she claimed—

slide a bureau up against it. Knowing Heather, I was surprised she hadn't kicked him in the balls. Then how would she have been able to fend him off if she had? She was nobody's fool.

While growing up, Franny became the steady member of our family—never exhibiting too many highs or lows—except on stage, where she would positively soar, like in a presentation of *Fame*, sitting at a piano, lone spotlight upon her, playing and singing "Out Here On My Own." That might have been the last time I cried.

But the Saturday of Heather's visit featured an anomaly to my sister's usual even-keeled demeanor—for Franny could not disguise her rage.

"Stay here!" she told Heather before marching off to confront her mother.

Franny's shouts could be heard from across the street, though I couldn't make out what she said.

While waiting, Heather messed up my collection of Topps baseball cards and moved most of the stuff I'd placed in precise order on the top of my desk. She pissed me off so much I stormed off to the Indian Trail.

When I returned, Mom and Franny were huddled over the kitchen table in hushed conversation.

Dad was at a tile job in Everett and I hadn't realized Heather was still there until I walked into the guest room and found her in a recliner, legs flopped over the side, watching *Partridge Family* reruns. Every time I changed the channel, she'd get up, turn it again, and plop back down—that infuriating Yankee cap propped on her head. My father had this thing about not wearing hats in the house—in fact, it could more appropriately be labeled an obsession—but he'd look at Heather, melt, and make an exception.

To this day, I don't know what Franny—and possibly my dad—said to Heather's mother. From what I understood, the string of "Papas" no longer showed up, or no one caught them if they did. Despite having an office in nearby Chelsea, Social Services wasn't a factor then—especially in the inner cities. I would've liked to believe that Heather's mom stopped inviting those men over because of love for her daughter—but even the non-skeptics among us were not that gullible. More likely, Mrs. Tierney altered her behavior due to an overriding affection for her monthly check and the dread of losing it.

Soon, Mom fell into the habit of setting a place at dinner time for Heather. Some nights Orlando would come by, pull up a chair and relate escapades that occurred in his garage. Heather—seldom at a loss for words when hanging out or playing ball at Frederick's Park—usually kept quiet. My brother, and occasionally my dad, were the only ones who could draw her out of that funk. For the duration of those meals, their inherent mission was to get her to laugh. This struck me as peculiar. Prior to that, during most of our dinners, my father would contribute to family conversations only periodically. Two- or three word-grunts mostly—like the churning sound a hotel lobby ice machine makes every fifteen minutes or so.

My mother's challenge was uniquely her own, for she could never figure out why—no matter how much she fed Heather, pushed second helpings on her—the girl hardly gained a pound. "Must be your high metabolism," Mom would say. And Ma grew discouraged when the clothes she brought home— outfits purchased at Bradlees where she worked part time—never quite fit Heather.

A shift occurred with the other guys in the gang. It couldn't be declared a major fault-line adjustment, but they—Damian particularly—backed off their consistent ragging of Heather. I was never sure if Damian got wind of something specific or sensed the darkness she'd been carrying. He quickly became fascinated by Heather's newfound ability to puke on demand—most times, without ever having to stick a finger down her throat. Those types of talents impressed him. He could extend his belches significantly beyond a minute. Sometimes after lunch, while our class silently took a test, he'd let one escape and then look up harmlessly—well, as harmless as an overgrown lug like Damian could look—and say, "Sorry, Miss O'Donnell."

And though Damian could be gross—and would never have been mistaken for someone who was kind—he wasn't a perv.

— 32 —

One afternoon later that summer, Scott, Tim and I were supposed to rent an outboard from Holt's Pier and fish near the breakwater. When we got to Tim's house, Mrs. Cote answered the door, announced he was grounded, and also let us know she'd piled on a bunch of chores to his regular weekend list.

We hadn't figured out what he was being punished for. The MDC police had raided the Pasteur schoolyard a few nights before, rounded up the kids who'd been drinking, and collected the names of a few others. Tim claimed he'd slipped away, but someone could've ratted on him.

We'd almost reached the pier when Heather bounded from Buzzy's corner store—four pieces of red licorice dangled from her lips.

"Want one?" She took a stick and handed it to me.

"Er. No thanks."

"Where you going?"

"Nowhere," Scott and I said in tandem. Fishing poles over each of our shoulders. Large green tackle box clearly evident in my hand.

"Can I come?"

"To nowhere?" I said with bite. "Sure. Scott, give Heather the directions to nowhere."

"Don't be a jerk all your life." And then, without invitation, she tagged along.

"Do you even know how to fish?" I asked. When my real question should've been, "Do you know how to be less annoying?" or "Can you swim?"

"How hard could it be? I've watched *Sea Hunt;* I've seen *Flipper.*"

"Jesus," Scott said.

After reaching Holt's, we were paying for the rentals when I turned to Heather. "Do you have money at least?" Of course, I knew the answer and felt immediate remorse for putting her on the spot like that.

I paid for her pole.

Scott hopped on board; I took Heather's hand and guided her down the pier's poor excuse for a ladder and onto the boat. Then I untied the line, pushed it away from the dock, and quickly jumped in.

257

The fourteen-foot skiff, equipped with a sixteen horsepower motor, hosted a few small leaks—nothing unusual, all of Holt's rentals did. Though not seaworthy in a true sense—especially if trapped by a surprise swell—it was adequate for what we intended: fishing close to the breakwater, with the shore still in view.

In those days, flounder were plentiful. You merely had to let your line drop lightly on the sandy bottom and troll leisurely. Pollock were another thing there was almost too much of—a "garbage" fish some of the cranky old guys used to call it, as they hung out at the pier, drank fifths of whiskey, and smoked unfiltered cigarettes.

We dropped anchor. Before long, Scott hauled in a few flounder, me a couple of Pollock—although in retrospect, I wondered if it could've been the same stupid fish I kept tossing back in.

Heather caught nothing but sunburn. "This sucks." A Winston smoldered between her fingers; her Yankee cap was twisted to the side.

By then, she'd taken her life jacket off, rolled her dungarees above her knees and tied her already soaking wet blouse up in a knot, so she exposed most of her belly. Sea spray glistened on her naked skin; soft waves lapped the boat's hull; we drifted until the anchor's chain pulled taut, and its metal clicked.

My insides stirred at the sight of Heather's bare midriff.

Scott, sitting at the bow and facing in the opposite direction, cast his line again. Its weight made a plopping sound.

"What are you looking at?" Heather said.

"Nothing."

What was wrong with me? I knew my face now sported the same shade of red as the back of her neck did. But there they were once more—those gorgeous brown eyes full of pain and longing. And I yearned to kiss her—no matter how revolted I tried to convince myself I was.

I turned and delivered a raspy spit off the stern— sounding as though a bug had touched down on my lips—then focused my attention on the shore and the many swimmers dotting the sand. A double-decker Ferris wheel loomed in the background.

Scott landed several more—for he'd possessed a trait few of us did at that age, the key ingredient to being a good fisherman: patience.

Something finally tugged on Heather's line. But she was no longer holding it by then, having placed it beside her.

"Grab it. I'll have to pay, if you lose it," I shouted.

Most of her pole had been drawn into the sea. Heather snagged the grip with her right hand just before it slipped out of reach, then held on with both.

With Heather's grasp fixed on the handle as tight as possible and Scott and me encouraging her, the scene unfolded like a kid's version of those *National Geographic* specials you'd see on TV Sunday afternoons. After a few minutes of play—more give and take—the fish broke the surface. Not a big-game marlin by any stretch, still, she'd hooked a decent-sized Cod. Scott helped, and after a while, Heather reeled the fish—over a foot and a half—onboard. It flopped around for a bit—nearly escaping—until I could snatch it and unhook its mouth.

Without missing a beat, Heather seized her prize from me and stood up; the dory rocked frantically, and she adjusted her balance.

"Careful," Scott yelled.

"My first catch ever." Heather beamed. She stretched out her arm and trophy, striking a pose *Angler's Journal* would've loved to have grace its cover.

"Alright," Scott said. "Hand it over so I can tie it up with the others and hang them off the side."

Heather leaned towards Scott, lost her equilibrium, sought to right herself, then fell overboard.

Instinctively, I lunged across to take hold of her, and the boat flipped over.

When Scott and I surfaced, he actually laughed before saying, "Jesus Christ."

A flock of seagulls—that'd been following us—flew overhead, dive bombing for our string of fresh catch, which gradually sank.

"Where's Heather?" I screamed.

We plunged beneath the surface. The seabed could have only been about twelve feet away at that point. And an elevated sandbar—which at dead low tide allowed beachgoers to walk half the distance to the Nahant peninsula, three miles away—lay below. But the tide wasn't low and twelve feet of water at the deep end of Cheryl Proto's swimming pool is a lot different than the same depth when it's on the Northeast coast of the Atlantic Ocean.

The sky, growing overcast, diminished visibility; but I dove in a few more times anyway. Raunchy-tasting, seaweed-strewn salt water filled my nose and mouth. We bobbed near the overturned boat, fought to tip it right side up without success, then managed to raise an end high enough to ensure Heather wasn't trapped there.

Two life jackets drifted out from underneath before the boat slid from our grasp. I couldn't be sure if one of those was the jacket Heather had removed or the two Scott and I had never put on—studs we thought we were.

I took hold of one and slipped it under my right arm.

Scott dove again.

Specks from the shore amplified—a swarm of potential saviors edged our way. Two rescue vessels—one with pontoons, the other a larger outboard—raced towards us.

I called for Heather. Even as I voiced her name, I realized it was a ludicrous gesture. Red and blue lights flashed on the sand. My arms and legs grew exhausted . . . dead weight, no longer a part of the rest of my body. I longed to detach from my limbs somehow. Remembering what that cute Red Cross instructor at Short Beach taught me, I stopped treading water, and floated for a few moments—hoping the respite might infuse me with some strength.

Scott wasn't in sight, so I hollered for him too. We needed to dive back in, but I could barely feel my arms, and he didn't answer me. Floating in the breakwater's direction, I snapped on the other life jacket strap. The swells weren't extremely rough; still, my shoulder slammed against a rock and excruciating throbs made me believe I'd broken it. When I grabbed another boulder to pull myself on top of the smoother plane, my palm smashed into a colony of barnacles; the fleshy pad of my hand stung and bled. By the time I could sit up, two crafts—manned by the MDC and fire rescue—together with a few other boats, had circled the area.

"Cut your engines," someone roared through a megaphone, and then an eerie silence fell, or I'd suddenly lost my hearing.

I sensed something overhead; waves chopped. A helicopter landed on the beach. Men from the MDC launch pulled a limp figure from the water.

Scott's black pants gave him away.

A small row boat approached the breakwater and got perilously close. A stout, familiar-looking man with salt-and-pepper hair—Mr. Graf, Vernon's father, from our neighborhood fire station—mouthed words. I didn't—couldn't—move.

A Yankee baseball cap floated by; it lingered in wave suds forming along a jetty of rocks before drifting out to sea.

— 33 —

The paramedics revived Scott while he still lay on their boat. A helicopter ferried him off to Mass General Hospital. By the following week, I was told he had come home, thank God.

Told because I remember little of the remains of that summer. I must've been present at Heather's funeral, yet memories of it reappeared only in brief somnambulant flashes. She would have scoffed at the pomp and circumstance death brings anyway.

For a long time, I retreated to my bedroom, listened to records and slept. My parents left me alone—out of wisdom, fear, or embarrassment, I'll never know. I'd become a kind of mute, letting music and lyrics do most of my thinking, feeling, and speaking for me. Adorned with the oversized bumble-bee-like headphones of the era, I'd play Young's "Cowgirl in the Sand" and "Down by the River" over and over again—the scratchy distortion of Neil's lead guitar at full blast. I wore stereo needles dull by playing Dylan's *Blonde on Blonde* and *Highway '61 Revisited* albums—later to discover he was singing about himself in "Like a Rolling Stone": "an endless stream of vomit," he once called it.

That form of self-hatred and isolation didn't seem alien to me.

I buried myself for hours in that room. Pored over lyrics and liner notes, boring the few visitors I'd been willing to see by sharing bootleg outtakes, offering insights and background on the meanings of songs, who played what instrument, who wrote what tune, who'd gone to bed with whom, and countless other tidbits that couldn't possibly matter to anyone else. Whenever the malady of silence and reflection reared its ugly head, I'd prescribe a dose of music or rock 'n' roll trivia and, if that didn't work, offbeat attempts at humor would follow.

I ate less and less until my mother pleaded with me to try, saying, with genuine alarm, "I can count your ribs." In the end, she convinced Dad to take me to a medical doctor—evidently, *those* kinds of doctors were OK—who prescribed a multivitamin and high-carb diet and sent us on our way.

I needed to cram my thoughts with anything that could drown out the emptiness I felt. My recurring memory of that afternoon at the breakers was the abrupt quiet. Those images stood as my personal Zapruder film—except mine played on a perpetual loop in black and white—a slow-motion movie that had lost its audio feed projected a few frames at a time. I *saw* my shoulders slam against the breakwater, the barnacle-covered boulders shred what remained of that flimsy life jacket—its pull strings jerked and tugged—blood seep from my palm, outboards stopping and restarting, boats crossing each other's wakes in a fury, scurrying cops, fire, and coastguardsmen pressing megaphones to their lips, Mister Graf moving in my direction, yet I *heard* nothing. A deafening silence blanketed me.

Against medical advice, my parents insisted on taking me from the Revere Memorial emergency room that very night. My father helped me slip out of the hospital Johnny and maneuver my newly cast arm and hypothermic body into dry clothes; at home, Ma filled me up on escarole soup. It didn't seem odd to them, I guess, that they were forced to give me directions via an improvised sign language and hand motions. *Shock,* I think they termed it back then.

My hearing returned within a few days . . . but I spoke little. I don't know if I'd really snapped out of it until the end of tenth grade—maybe much later.

Even as an adult, there were times when I was not sure I'd escaped that trauma completely. I wondered if I ever would.

Strange things followed—evidence of what you might call collateral damage: my terrified reaction to loud gushes of water streaming in the sink; tremors at the sound of helicopter blades; my refusal to take showers—only baths. And these represented a mere sample of illogical behaviors. Mr. Gallagher, our freshman track coach, was familiar with my history, so when my mother told him I had a skin condition and couldn't shower with the other guys, he went along with that charade. The next year's baseball coach was not as understanding, and I would soon grow to miss my favorite sport, leaving in mid-season and never trying out for another team in high school. Orlando was clearly destined to be *the* jock in the family—especially in football and hockey—so maybe I'd presumed by failing, or not participating, I could knock my dad down a few pegs.

Not long thereafter, a weird sensation overcame me. Similar to when your ears plug up and the pressure in your head gets heavy. So you're instructed to pinch your nose and squeeze, to force a yawn, or to chew gum to clear out that stuffiness, and then you'd be able to take deep breaths and hear again. No

267

home remedy made a speck of difference; I would be blocked for years.

The rituals one would naturally expect me to avoid I stopped—like swimming in Cheryl's pool and at Revere Beach. I'd only visit Short Beach on the Winthrop end, a good distance away from the tattered amusements and the "curve" where my friends and I once dived. Every so often, I went clamming and collected bottles for return money. Most times though, I'd gaze out at the horizon and linger near the shore.

Again and again, Orlando and Franny raged at our mother and father—insisting they seek help for me. These arguments grew so vociferous and happened so frequently that I'd keep my headphones on—well after a record album had finished playing.

My parents—Dad particularly—would have none of it, the mere mention of counseling akin to blasphemy. *He* couldn't confront it. With what *people* might think. How it could fuck me up more. How I might end up in one of *those places.*

"Look at him," he'd say to my sister and brother. "Good grades. Doesn't get into trouble—will ya just look at him. He'll be fine."

But my showering phobia irked Dad—the final straw. He'd even call me a "pansy" or "a Mary" sporadically until my mother shamed him into a type of rapprochement. When it got back to me that my quitting the baseball team had pissed him off, I wasn't sorry.

A few months later, six-pack in hand, my father led me across the street to the Indian trail. He spoke about a garden he tended to as a kid—tomatoes, string beans, radishes, lettuce, and carrots—and how his Irish, French, and Jewish friends used to tease him and spew "Dago peasant farmer" as well as other pleasant epithets at him.

And, at my father's funeral, when Uncle Tony revealed a number of challenges Dad had encountered while in the South Pacific, I grieved but also felt disappointment that he hadn't possessed a deeper insight into what I might've been going through—on a much smaller scale. But who knew what standards his own parents and military comrades had indoctrinated him with, where those goalposts had been fixed?

Francesca never could forgive him—for reasons I understood. Before he died, I had learned to, mainly hoping to provide him—and me—with some mode of neutrality, a measure of peace.

Gradually, through the love of my siblings—and

Johanna—a healing transpired. I had hoped my story would turn out like those anecdotes you sometimes heard in which the subject suffered a leg fracture, yet hadn't realized it. Sooner or later, the bone set, the injured party continued to walk—perhaps with a slight limp—and, over time, it had been scarcely noticeable.

Most days, it was as if all of this had happened to a different person; I'd been hauling a stranger's legacy.

I no longer played sports during high school and no longer swam, but picked up cross-country in college and often raced along the Charles River or—years later—on a rail trail near Orlando's house. It occurred to me during an outing on a path in my brother's Topsfield neighborhood that Johanna was always sprinting and searching *for* that one elusive place, that one state of being, while I'd been running *away* from it.

— 34 —

When Aubrey wiped something from the corner of her eye, I reached out to hold her hand and immediately regretted I'd shared the events of that long-ago afternoon. An unfair burden to unload on a new girlfriend—even though she'd been a friend-friend for quite a while—after listening to my tale of woe, she must've assumed a loony had been dropped upon her doorstep.

It was also the ultimate betrayal.

If I were destined to reveal that story to anyone, it should have been Johanna. Of course, my immediate family lived most of it—or, at least, Orlando and Franny, the two people who'd bothered to *see* me. I felt lighter—if not entirely relieved—after baring it. Once I started to speak to Aubrey, I couldn't figure out a way to stop—over twenty years of anguish and repressed memories were unleashed.

The most unexpected and, dare I say, pleasant surprise was how regardless of our differences—

tastes in music and literature, sense of worth—my revelation, confession really, brought Aubrey and me closer together. Rather than retreating, she refused to leave my side. I hadn't deserved that type of loyalty, that level of affection, but vowed to do my best to honor it.

On that day, we hugged in silence for what seemed liked hours; then walked the length of Newbury Street, through the Public Garden and back, hand in hand. No doubt we spoke during our stroll, but I can't remember a single word.

Despite Aubrey's continuing efforts to offer comfort, feelings of self-recrimination and more tumbled from me like stolen TVs and radios from a box truck parked in a back alley of my childhood: guilt, for having revealed this chapter of my history and, by doing so, saddling it on Aubrey; remorse for some of the anger I continued to direct towards my parents all those years later—they weren't in the boat; it wasn't their fault for not insisting Heather put on her life-jacket; humiliation for my weakness; shame at my vigilant attempts to push Heather as far from my mind as I could; regret for being selfish enough to think my hardships were worse than most other people's and not appreciating the fact I had it better than others; disingenuousness for not copping to this and other vulnerabilities with Johanna from the start; and culpability for not owning the pain.

"Welcome to the human race. It had to be lonely out there by yourself," Aubrey said when I conveyed my rambling, swirling jumble of ideas a few days later. "Next Thanksgiving, we may even let you sit at the adult table." She gave me a prolonged hug and kiss.

Without Aubrey's support, it would not have been possible to overcome the North Shore code of silence instilled in me during my youth.

Early on, I'd considered telling Johanna about these fears of mine, but could never find the right opportunity and dreaded the thought of ruining one of the few moments we'd had the chance to be together during our limited and apportioned time slots. I'd reasoned she already had too much to deal with.

Aubrey encouraged me to meet with a counselor—although this wasn't stipulated as a condition for us to continue our relationship. I half-heartedly protested. She wasn't the only person who recognized it might've been a step long overdue. Because of that, I hesitated; after all, we were talking about an episode that had occurred well over two decades earlier.

I made a therapy appointment with a person recommended by Aubrey's doctor.

Everybody wants to build and nobody wants to do maintenance. This was the Vonnegut quote that hung on a sign in my new therapist's office and I considered it a good omen. Once I overcame my irritation with those white noise devices—that were anything but soothing initially—and my embarrassment for sometimes running into other clients in the waiting room, and the anxiety caused by our mostly silent first couple of visits, I appreciated the experience. Yet—as Johanna would concur—a skeptic can rarely be cured.

Dr. Richardson—an erudite and nonjudgmental professional with no skin in the game—listened, had a name for some of my behavior patterns, and assisted me in understanding these quirks hadn't been unique to my situation. Apparently, one disorder she ID'ed, psychogenic deafness, was a method for the body to shut out trauma.

"It was protection," Dr. R told me, smiling, before lapsing into a Dr. Ruth Westheimer impersonation when she explained the syndrome—the only occasion I ever remember my therapist letting her guard down in front of me.

I had "homework," as she called it, and those assignments focused on self-compassion, acceptance, and goal planning. We spent most of our time discussing "avoidant" tendencies and methods of possibly conquering them. This meant overcoming my inclination to steer clear of circumstances, people, places—even thoughts—reminding me of "that day."

Though next to impossible, I strove to approach these exercises with an open mind.

Eventually, Dr. Richardson helped nurture reminiscences of Heather unconnected to the accident. Visions of her came to me with much more frequency: her rifling a throw to first base on the Frederick's Park diamond, smoking a Winston on the Indian trail, and arguing fervently that Yankee player Thurman Munson was "ten times better" than Red Sox catcher Carlton Fisk.

In the end, the most important gift I received from Dr. R was her being more than willing to let me off the hook, not only for my past but also for informing her I wouldn't be returning—after we'd participated in about four months of treatment.

"You've had enough guilt for two lifetimes," she said.

My involvement with therapy had been like working at carpentry with Orlando when I did my best to assist him with the platform bed. I had no prior background, no frame of reference, and little— or no—tools to work with. The enthusiasm I periodically displayed when explaining to my brother and a few others the baby steps I'd taken embarrassed me. Nevertheless, those sessions with Dr. R. did have their merits.

Aubrey was upset with me for bailing on the appointments. Unlike Dr. Richardson, she didn't refrain from telling me so and why.

"You have to unburden your mind. And, begin again."

"I'm too stubborn for any sort of rebirth. Besides, you can't teach an old dog—"

"—Bullshit! Absolute crap."

Far from being offended by Aubrey's unfiltered honesty, I wouldn't have had it any other way. But if I was slated to move forward, ending counseling seemed to be the right path for me; and, more importantly, it had been one of my own choosing.

Aubrey got over it and would place small replicas of Buddha on my bookcases and scented candles on the fireplace mantel—alongside my father's drawing of Mister Peabody and Sherman. She'd also slip self-help and "mindfulness" titles and flyers on the end tables. Much later, she urged me to visit Revere Beach in order to say a prayer for Heather, Scott . . . and also me.

So on a Sunday afternoon, we rode on the subway and she stopped to buy a bunch of flowers at the Government Center train station. When they didn't have the particular species she sought, Aubrey led me up the escalator to a floral shop a few blocks down the street. At first, she searched for gladiolas which—according to her—signified "remembrance." She couldn't find those, so we settled for pink—not red, nor white—only pink carnations because, Aubrey assured me, they implied "I'll never forget you."

We arrived at the beach and held a brief memorial service near the shore's edge. Afterwards, Aubrey put my hand in hers and tenderly guided me out on top of the breakwater. She glanced at the faded wound on my left hand. "Nearly gone."

"Almost," I agreed and tossed my flowers.

Gulls dive bombed, disappointed we hadn't brought food.

The first time I'd stepped foot on the breakwater since that day, I camped in the middle of the rock formation while Aubrey ventured twenty yards further from shore and threw her share of carnations into the ocean.

Pieces of a lobster trap floated into an outcrop of boulders, then locked inside them. Wood slats, netting, and buoy parts sloshed back and forth. I wasn't able to remain on the rocks for too long. Perhaps only five minutes passed before I grew light-headed and disoriented; my knees trembled. Still, I wanted to believe this ritual would help. Not while I was standing there, not when I retreated to the sandy shore after a few moments . . . and maybe not even later that evening, but, with the encouragement of friends, this skeptic would find a way to unearth faith.

In the weeks that followed, I paid a visit to my mother to try to understand why she and my dad hadn't gotten me some support. Ma had been rubbing that ancient, oversized kitchen table with a damp dishrag in repetitive circular motions — scrapes and scuffs left by thousands of meals embedded in its walnut. She appeared intent on removing the finish if I'd let her. I grasped her arm to interrupt, and we both edged slowly into chairs at opposite ends of the table.

Ma sighed. Clothes tumbled in a nearby dryer.

Unsure what to do next, I studied a tall hutch that stood against the wall behind her. Besides drawers filled with silverware, and doors opening to china reserved for special occasions and holidays, two shelves held cookbooks featuring Betty Crocker dinners, *Good Housekeeping* soups, and Pillsbury desserts—along with spiral-bound folders stuffed with snatches of paper containing handwritten recipes and those clipped from newspapers and magazines. Stored amid these were a small number of books from the children's Landmark Series. My mother had given them to me on birthdays and Christmases from the moment I learned to speak. Covered in bold-colored dust jackets with vibrant images, they relayed tales of extraordinary people and events. *Guadalcanal Diaries*, *The Story of the Marines*, and *Women of Courage* were some titles I could make out that day. Several others—*The First Transatlantic Cable*, *George Washington Carver*, *Sante Fe Trail*, *JFK-PT109* and more—were scattered in rooms throughout the house and buried in some of my own moving boxes and bins I still hadn't disturbed.

Mom would write my full name—Matthew Alexander Dominico—the date, and perhaps a few words of encouragement on their title pages. She hoped to show me what I "could become" and I'd never been sure if I had imagined it, but more of these books seemed to arrive after what had happened to Heather.

"To say your father came home from the War a changed man wouldn't do it justice. The kid I fell for in high school was gone," she said. "We married soon after he returned because that had been the plan after all—and your father 'always kept his promises' he said. He'd putter in the cellar listening to Sinatra sing 'Time After Time' or Dean Martin's 'Return to Me'— or maybe some Glenn Miller stuff. And I couldn't reach him."

She folded and unfolded the rag before staring at the self-portrait caricature of my dad on the wall. "He had dreams of what was supposed to happen. Some of which he shared in letters to me. That might've given him hope."

Then she told me my grandfather took sick—and later my grandmother. That my father knew "he had a duty" and "no GI Bill would take care of that." His uncle Al got him into the tile union—"a good and steady trade." And, at some point, they'd heard about Rudy, my father's best friend from the Navy. His family had thrown him out. The VFW guys let him sleep in the storage room of the Post while he per- formed odd jobs and custodial duties. People started to complain—not so much about Rudy's drinking, but the damage he'd cause after waking with night terrors or when having flashbacks.

"So Rudy stayed with us for a few years. Those nightmares of his grew worse and frightened you kids—especially you."

I hadn't thought of my Dad's friend in decades. He wore a dull, gold-colored watch equipped with a jumbo dial and second-hand set beneath its cracked lens. When I was in third grade, Rudy would remove it from his wrist on weekday afternoons, sit on our sun porch, and record the time it took for me to run home at the close of school day. He'd enter my results in a small steno notebook—the kind bookies used to keep track of client bets at Joe the Barber's—then encourage me to improve my performance. Written in perfect Palmer penmanship, those pages were marked with entries like "Monday: 2 minutes 47 seconds-Heavy rain." Rudy also spent days with Orlando working on a Chevy Bel Air model kit they'd picked up at the drug store. It wasn't long before I'd lose interest in their endeavor and walk away.

A purple finch struck the hour by warbling from an Audubon clock that hung in Mom's kitchen.

"We finally drove Rudy to the in-patient psych unit at the Soldier's Home and your dad wouldn't budge. Just sat with his head on the steering wheel, while the nurse and me wheeled him inside.

"Your father's impatience intensified—over minor things as well as big."

He once ripped out an entire wall of tile because of two fractured pieces that could have "easily been replaced separately."

My mother told me about a Sunday morning drive along the beach in Swampscott—black smoke sputtering from our old Rambler. She smiled wryly and spoke of a house with green shutters—embellishments that never graced a window in our neighborhood—and a front yard with rose trellises and a pear tree.

"He pulled me close and said, 'One day, we'll leave Revere and you'll live in a place like this. I promise.' The plans he had . . . Then Orlando, our scholarship athlete son—with an IQ off the charts—not only quits college, but starts working at a gas station down the street. Soon he buys the damn joint. Franny falls for a girl. And you . . ."

She fiddled with wooden salt and pepper shakers my sister had carved in elementary school and given to her for Mother's Day—Jack-o'-lanterns with over-sized chef's hats.

The dryer's timer buzzed. Startled, I looked towards the laundry.

"I'm not sure you can understand, Matt. I didn't want to become another disappointment in his life.

So I avoided crossing him whenever I could. . . .and should have fought for you—for us. . . . Sorry." She covered part of her face with the rag; drops of moisture from the towel dripped onto the table, pooling in its scars.

That afternoon might've been the first-time I'd thought of Ma as a single woman—a person who once flourished outside of my orbit. I reflected on the myriad possibilities that had been opened to her.

When my parents entertained friends and relatives, voices grew boisterous, conversations more raucous as night wore on. These discussions were peppered with *figurati, basta,* and other Italian colloquialisms—along with the notorious Boston accent Hollywood always seemed to butcher. But Ma consistently maintained her *sotto voce* tone—absent any discernable dialect. Every so often, people were forced to ask her to stop and repeat something. It was a trait that could cause my father to halt—mid tirade—during his high decibel arguments.

I had never pondered whether this speech pattern of hers had been schooled, triggered by reticence, or due to how she might have viewed her standing in the world. What I did notice during those rare occasions when she offered an opinion—like the diffident question, "Don't you think it's a matter of fairness?"—the volume in the room dropped, and folks paused to listen.

I wondered if Mom ever regretted not giving my dad a couple of books from that Landmark series to let him see what he could have still been, and avoid having him despise—with each passing day—what he had become. But I said nothing further concerning the subject to her that night—or even later. I was certain neither of us expected a cathartic Kumbaya moment and little good would come from more anger; this much I understood.

I'd assumed I reached some sort of peace with my parents, yet remained disillusioned and confused by my father's actions. Having been through the traumas of war, he, of all people, might've empathized. It was a reminder to me there would inevitably be questions without answers: a lesson I'd first been taught at fourteen, frightened, cold, and wet while hunched precariously on top of a wave-battered breakwater.

Aubrey could recite by heart passages from Joan Didion's *Slouching towards Bethlehem,* as well as works by Anais Nin, Erica Jong, Gail Sheehy, and others to the point of driving me absolutely batty, and though she'd rather listen to Metallica or Guns N' Roses than the Moody Blues—we both had a love of the PBS shows: *This Old House*, *NOVA*, and *Austin City Limits*; and she was on board with my view of Jackson Browne, as well as a relatively new guy named Prince. So we stayed together for another three years—because she cared for me and I her. But, contrary to popular opinion, common interests, similar hobbies and tastes, don't always a deep relationship make.

Frequently, couples separate, and these breakups are not necessarily marked by fireworks, trauma, or rage.

Aubrey had outgrown me. I'd been holding back her incredible store of fire and energy, and she stood by my side out of loyalty. She'd begun to perform publicist duties for a number of musicians and had also garnered attention for her work on several AIDS-related benefits. When singer Billy Marshall thanked Aubrey at the Paradise and publicly acknowledged her efforts, she ducked behind me. I had to nudge her forward repeatedly before she'd join him on stage.

At a club launch we attended, I ran into Sheila Giannino. Pleased at first, I later grew disheartened. Some guy's hands were wrapped securely around her waist—a little too rigidly, I thought—like a stern parent prohibiting his kid from mingling with others at a backyard birthday celebration. It was Andy Fox, whose father was "connected" and once owned a few dives on the boulevard. I'd heard Andy had been released from jail recently after doing years of hard time. This reunion saddened me. The narrative I'd concocted in my head for Sheila had always been she married a successful software engineer and they lived happily together with their 2.5 kids on the coast of Southern Maine.

One afternoon, Aubrey burst through the apartment door. Her keys splashed with a clang on a small kitchen table she bought for me after sharing too many dinners on TV trays—or on the floor covered by that questionable blue rug.

"Guess what!" That Renaissance-Faire grin of hers shined.

Aubrey gave me no time to offer a response.

"I scored tickets to the Prince concert. It's tonight. At the Centrum—and we've got VIP passes!"

I glanced out the window at our laundry-lady neighbor—hoping to hide my disappointment. Though off that night, I had been putting in extra hours at Medical Records and had a deadline looming for some album reviews I'd been working on. The idea of renting a car, schlepping to Worcester, then getting home well after midnight didn't excite me. Besides, although only four years older than Aubrey and not quite jaded, I'd already seen the movie. Yet I hadn't the heart to tell her.

She somehow read my mind.

"Look at you. The bags under your eyes. It's OK. I'll give them to someone at *The Phoenix*—we'll order Chinese. Rent a video, stay here and watch a flick."

I'm not sure what made me feel more terrible: how old I must've looked at that moment or how selfish I felt.

"Take Eric."

She worked with him at the paper. Younger than Aubrey, he was clean cut, earnest and green. At the handful of social events we'd been to together, I'd witnessed him stop in his tracks whenever Aubrey spoke and gaze at her in amazement—as if the words she were speaking had never been uttered before. I understood that feeling.

"Nah, it's fine." But then the shine in her eyes that had dimmed flickered again. "You really think it'll be alright?"

"Of course."

Later that night—well, actually early morning the next day—Aubrey's key clicked softly in the door. I'd been sitting in the living room reading. After being on the 11-to-7 shift for such an extended period, I sometimes had difficulty falling asleep on nights I wasn't on the schedule.

Aubrey opened the refrigerator; the emanating light shone upon her beaming face. When she turned and saw me in the easy chair, her glow faded abruptly—like a motion detector spotlight that unexpectedly turns off—though the fridge was still ajar.

"I'm sorry," she said.

"For what?"

"I should have stayed home."

And she started to cry.

I knew Aubrey had not slept with Eric.

Just like I knew I would always be delighted by that initial bite into an Emack & Bolio waffle cone, would never tire of the viselike hugs Orlando's kids gave me, and would hold on to some level of current from the spark of energy that struck me on the very first day I met Aubrey at the record store. Why I was so certain she hadn't gone to bed with him, I couldn't explain.

It was worse than that.

Still, I said, "It's OK." I edged Aubrey over to the

sofa, and comforted her—as if discovering a three-year love affair and relationship was now over would ever be OK.

And for a moment I considered telling Aubrey the truth: that our breakup probably wouldn't be resolved painlessly and swiftly, that the both of us might hurt until we woke one morning and were able to focus on something else first before facing the new day, and—rather than diminish entirely—after lengthy intervals of remission, this ache would return in slight piercing, surprising, and unexpected jabs.

For the time being at least, "OK" seemed to be the appropriate response.

So we held each other on that Bob's Discount special and, when dawn broke, we stepped outside, huddled to brace ourselves against the chill, and took a stroll towards the Public Garden. This walk almost mirrored the one we made the day I told Aubrey about Heather.

I hoped I'd provided an anchor for Aubrey in a phase of need and growth, showed her how much she'd helped not only me but her friends and the people she answered in her advice columns. I also fought—with a passion that surprised me—to get her over the remorse about the anger she'd harbored for her mother. Though she had no reason to feel guilty, it would take a higher power than me to help Aubrey understand she was not to blame for how her childhood turned out.

She gave me solace, support, and love when I'd been desperate and in little—or no—supply of all three and I'd be forever grateful.

Aubrey continued to call me occasionally when a favorite author was appearing at a local bookstore, and we wound up attending a Peggy Rambach and Joe Torra reading—as well as some others. Several months ago, she invited me to the Brattle, where the King Vidor and De Laurentis' version of *War and Peace*—the one we'd seen years before—was being shown. I politely declined, assuring her that, this time, I was certainly the person who would doze off.

— 35 —

Just before her daughter's first birthday, Johanna sent me a homemade card. A picture she'd taken of Faith—replete with her mom's curls—graced its cover. Subsequent holiday greetings, along with the occasional Christmas note—the kind you sometimes got that let you know *Dick finally accepted the promotion that was offered, little Tammy has braces, and Madison's entering third grade and is a Girl Scout now*— also made their way to my mailbox for the next few years. Every so often, I'd receive one of those special handwritten letters from Jo which would contain an original sketch or Polaroid photo of paintings she'd been working on. I'd pore over their contents, read them again, rub the paper to feel the texture of the higher-than-normal-quality stock she'd written them on—at times even sniff, hoping to discover trace scents of peach shampoo—and periodically tape a snapshot to the fridge or mirror. Then, as to be expected, they stopped arriving.

I followed Johanna via art magazines and the Sunday *Globe* and *Times* culture sections and—as Internet searches became more common and accessible—through Yahoo and later Google, but those articles became scant.

Whenever I passed a railroad crossing or horseback rider—or saw a plant drooping and thirsty—I thought of Johanna. I'd routinely reflect on the Heraclitus maxim that once hung on a poster in Jo's bedroom, realize I was no longer in the same river, and do my best to accept it.

Orlando, my ever-present and dependable rock of a brother, had his own proverbs to deliver. If I hadn't shared the many beers together with his wisdom in the bay of his gas station, I wouldn't have survived and that's not hyperbole. In a section of his garage, Orlando had constructed a shelf on which he placed candles and a statue of Buddha. It wasn't a shrine per se; I guess it stood as a type of off-stage prompt for him. My brother is the most unflappable person I know, and it didn't seem weird to me even when this spiritual corner was viewed in the context of several topless girly wall calendars and Pennzoil posters. Though I did wonder what our devout Catholic grandmother might've thought.

After receiving an MA in Lit, I snagged a part-time job at a two-year college and continued to freelance. I enjoyed my students, had a decent—albeit tiny—condo near Belle Isle Marsh in East Boston, and what most would call a comfortable, if not entirely fulfilled, life. Never married, I remained open to the possibility, no matter "how late" it was getting, which Orlando, of the three kids and sore back, never hesitated to remind me.

I had a fairly regular gig as a stringer for a couple of local newspapers, was lucky enough to score the random magazine article, and had a collection of short stories published. The music-related essays and coverage, not so much. Concert reviews are a young person's game. With songs no longer being the factor they once were, I had difficulty getting excited about new artists. This was a healthy response to be sure, and I got to thinking it was sort of a foolish assignment to begin with—describing a musical event in writing, transposing a primarily audio presentation into words and pictures. How's that supposed to turn out when those performances depend little on the visual and—as Johanna fittingly said years before—more on soul? To justify those endeavors, I had hoped to become a champion for the struggling artist.

I had relished the task—a craving that needed to be fed. How definitively those efforts impacted the musicians, the fans, the readers, I'd never know. Jerry, a coworker at the *Real Paper*, loved to repeat the adage: *Today's news is tomorrow's fish wrap.*

At first I protested, before eventually realizing he was right.

I once argued with a writer friend—a guy who played in a garage band, someone whose work and opinion I valued—about how Pink had taken Joni Mitchell's singer-songwriter mantle and brought it to a whole other level. He laughed in my face, scoffed, and ridiculed me. It hurt. Why did that exchange with him affect me to such a degree? What did it matter? No one could disagree Mitchell was a superb talent and a member of royalty, whereas Pink—also boasting outstanding ability—possessed a different, no less legitimate, gift. Long after that vehement argument and loss of friendship, I realized that to me, still very much the kid from Revere, Pink's triumphs, her success, somehow validated the journeys, the struggles of all the Heathers I had known growing up. The chips on their shoulders—and mine—would never completely disappear, but Pink's championship struggle for the crown took a bit of the edge off.

A decade ago, my cousin Caroline called to let me know the last of her uncles (a brother of my late

Uncle Edward) had passed away and she wondered if I might want something from the estate. I couldn't think of anything, yet welcomed the opportunity to see the Wisconsin homestead and then swing over to Appleton.

Uncle Ed knew the owners of Mercury and Evinrude motors—both of whom were from the Fond du Lac area—and that acquaintanceship once triggered a discussion about whether a person could be wealthy and remain an honorable human being. Funny, I couldn't recall what side of the debate my uncle landed on, but appreciated the respect he afforded me. Later, he'd tell me of his passion for owls and how he'd sometimes measure his days and chores on the farm by where and when he saw them.

After checking in on the soon-to-be-sold family legacy, I drove to Appleton and walked along the Fox River, which bordered the cemetery. I looked out over a trail that had replaced the tracks Johanna once stood next to and stared at for hours until the two parallel rails merged into one and she imagined the many adventures and possibilities that lay beyond them.

Still on the Avon Gallery's mailing list, I discarded dozens of postcard invitations before finally deciding to take a ride there a few years ago—despite my vow to discover other rivers. I browsed in the exhibition space for forty-five minutes, then crossed the street and headed up the banks of the trestle where Johanna and I had waved to the engineer. Crumbled paper tumbled across tracks and ties before resting at my feet. I picked up an ink-smudged and tattered scrap which turned out to be an old New Haven and Northampton train schedule; it listed Milldale, Plainville, Avon, Simsbury, and several other Connecticut stations that had long since been forgotten.

A freight pulling boxcars full of plywood covered in white flapping sheets clicked and waddled by; I watched until it disappeared from view. An evening lark crooned. Though I had considered walking down Arch Road to find out if the country store and meadow were still there, I couldn't summon up the courage.

On the way to my car, I passed the entrance to Saint Anne's, was tempted to venture inside but thought better of it. Atop a trailer—parked on the spot where the church's community garden once flourished and a fountain gurgled—stood an alphabet sign which read *Let us love with actions and truth and not with words or speech.*—John 3:18.

The Catskills — 2012

Faith greets me at the door; but her mother's eyes return my gaze. Though she has wispier and much lighter-colored hair, there's no mistaking whose daughter she is. "You've got to be famished after that drive. Let me get you something to eat or drink."

After I refuse her kind offer, she brings me to a converted barn that stands about a hundred feet from the house. It appears to be a studio; several of Johanna's pieces—many of them framed—hang on the rough-hewn wooden walls. I'm led to a back room where picture windows face rolling hills and meadow. On three sides, thick forest borders this expanse of land, and on the left lies a large pond. A pastel self-portrait of a twenty-something Johanna leans against a section of wainscot.

In the far right-hand corner, the subject of that painting sits on a stool and adds light brush strokes to a landscape on the easel in front of her.

"Mom, this is Matt . . . a friend."

It's only after her daughter speaks that Johanna

turns around, looks at us and hesitates for a moment before saying a simple "Hey."

She pauses a few seconds more—perhaps there's a sign of recognition. Missing that sea-glass glint, her eyes still shine like pebbles in a crystalline stream. Then Johanna—hair primarily gray now—tilts her head slightly, as if pondering an answer to a quiz, before turning to scrutinize the canvas.

Faith tells me later how she and her husband would visit Johanna's apartment and discover a week's worth of dishes piled up in the sink or a pan containing the remnants of what was once soup or string beans lit on the burner but with the fluid boiled away. On subsequent trips, plants scattered in various rooms would cry out in desperate need of water and care.

"Clear, she was no longer safe, Andrew and I moved her. Mom must've understood on some level, though, because it took little convincing on our part. We kept most of her stuff and set up the studio. The barn had been pretty much empty anyway—nothing but a place to store clutter. We didn't have the chance to go through any of her things until a few weeks ago. That's when I found the box of your letters and postcards."

Johanna wanders into the kitchen without a sound. She smiles.

"You OK, Mom?"

"Just coffee."

She fiddles with the Keurig machine for a few minutes—opens its cover; places it down, pushes some buttons and raises the lid again, to no avail.

Faith makes her a cup. "Let me carry that. It's hot."

"I'll be right back," Faith says to me.

Johanna glances in my direction, whispers something that approximates "Thanks," grins, and leaves.

I exhale deeply. It seems as if I've been holding my breath since I first walked through their front door.

A small series of photographs and sketches rest on a shelf above their breakfast nook. Among them is a charcoal drawing of John Lennon—the top of the Empire State building looms in its background.

Later, Faith tells me a few years after Ted, her father, died, Johanna had shared a story about a man she loved who'd disappointed her.

"After a while, Mom conceded she'd disappointed him too. 'We let each other down' was how she phrased it. . . .When I skimmed through those letters—" She pauses, turns to me and says, "It appeared obvious who the man she was in love with. Sorry. I realize it was an intrusion. Andrew and I mulled over whether to reach out. Wondering what good it could do."

"I'm glad you did."

"With Mom slipping away, I owe it to her and . . . to you. What was—is—the right thing to do?"

Her eyes well up.

Having assisted Ma with my grandmother, who was in the advanced stages of dementia, I have a hunch of what the day-to-day toll has been and a notion of the anxiety Johanna's uncertain future has provoked in Faith.

She dabs her face with a tissue before assuring me that Johanna *does* still have interludes of lucidity and they greet those events like bright sunshine on otherwise chilly winter days.

"The past seems to be more vivid. Mom will begin by saying, 'Did I tell you about the time—?'" Faith laughs. "And that leads to a wonderful tale about a concert in the Village, an art exhibit, or an escapade that happened in Appleton.

"She sometimes speaks with such clarity. I fool myself into believing we have her back with us. Then there are times when she won't bathe, can't find her studio, gets belligerent—even violent—and demands to return to 'her place' the condo we've sold. Scary."

Faith shows me to a garden apartment in the barn where she's set me up for the night. "Stay as long as you wish."

I'm certain Faith's honestly thinking of her mom—and me—when she extends that invitation, yet the bags forming beneath her eyes and look of concern periodically checking in and out of her expressions, help me recognize she could also use a break.

Not long after we'd finish supper, Faith helped put her mother to bed.

Now I stand in the privacy of the bathroom separated not only by a number of walls and rooms, a thirty-yard stretch of lawn between house and barn, but by miles—too many to count—from Johanna.

A slow, steady drip from the sink nudges me out of my reverie. I wash both hands—pausing on the barely discernible pink spot on my left—before turning the handles to the faucets as tight as possible, eager to attain a silence that will allow me to gather my thoughts.

Something inside me breaks.

"What do *you* have to cry about?" I ask my reflection.

You've made your bed, No decision is a decision, and

a few more petty maxims and half-truths from Orlando and others flow. Even *Defer no time, delays have dangerous ends* from *Henry the Fourth* springs to mind; Professor Garber would be proud. I splash cold water on my face, then look at a bathrobe Faith has hung on the door hook for me. Wisconsin cows and cheese are conspicuously absent.

Days pass. Johanna still can't figure out who I am.

Faith tries to help. "Ma, you remember who this is? It's Matt, your friend from Boston."

I convince myself she recognizes me—or understands there's a link between us, a bond we once shared.

But Johanna's usual reply to her daughter's question is, "Of course, I do. He used to teach with me in Colorado . . . at the university . . . literature. He tells—writes—stories."

Close, Johanna, I reason. *Very close. Perhaps all along I've been better at telling 'em to myself—and anyone who'll listen—than at writing them down.*

I implore Faith to stop prodding her mom. She's making these efforts on my behalf to give me hope. And though I'm appreciative, it's having the opposite effect on me and those queries make Johanna anxious—as if she's failed another test and we're disappointed in her.

Most mornings and many afternoons, Johanna lets me take her by the arm and we meander through the meadow. She grows less predictable at dusk, so we don't venture out late. Every so often, we'll lean against a split-rail fence to watch the neighbor's horses. Johanna was skittish initially and dropped the first apple I handed her. Now I do my best to slice pieces with a small kitchen knife and she'll happily feed them.

During one of our walks back to the house, red-winged blackbirds cross the setting sun, and I am reminded of an afternoon I spent with Orlando. We sat on spartan lawn chairs in his backyard, heard a hawk screech, then a thud. Soon a sparrow wobbled onto my brother's driveway. Slipping from the clutches of the hawk, it had bounced off the roof before landing. The sparrow preened in some dust, stumbled for a few unsteady steps, and took flight.

"A *Revere* bird," Orlando said. He shook his head and laughed.

Occasionally, I drive Jo to doctors' appointments. No matter how frequently I try or reason or insist I'm able to see some sign, a glimpse, an indication the "old" Johanna is still *there* and, before long—with a

305

tad more nurturing—Faith, Andrew, and her other caretakers will also witness it too, they patiently humor and comfort me before saying, "That *probably* isn't going to be the case."

They just don't understand us.

I wonder what Johanna might think of her skeptic now.

One day, Faith takes me upstairs to the second story of the barn to reveal an immense panoramic project Johanna has been working on in stops and starts. It consists of at least eight panels of three-by-four foot canvases—portraying a formidable steam engine with connecting cars. Popping out from each of them are the upper halves of such figures as Anwar Sadat, Janis Ian, Arlo Guthrie, Marjorie Keller, Judy Chicago, Golda Meir, and others.

"The *Peace Train*. She keeps changing the destination." Faith points to discarded panels on the floor that feature railroad crossings and tunnels, beaches, empty sky, or subway and road signs: West 4th, South Station, Appleton, Avon, Boston and . . . Revere Beach.

I contact the college. This conversation doesn't go well at first; ultimately, I'm allowed to bail on my fall semester courses and the department chair suggests I notify HR to request an "official" LOA. Before ending the call, I have to ask her what the acronym means. I also reach out to Orlando to tell him I'll return to my condo this weekend to pick up some clothes and stuff.

"Can you help me sublet the place?"

"Sure."

My brother is understanding, and I'm not sure why I'm surprised by that.

He asks, "How long will you be out there?"

I don't have an answer. "We'll figure it out," I say when he presses me for one.

"At the end of the way is freedom. Till then, patience," Orlando says.

I could barely hear him.

Most nights, Johanna and I sit at Faith's battle-scarred upright piano with its intricate relief carvings of leaves, vines, and lions; they've all seen better days yet still impress. While on our knees together, we've already plowed through dozens of sheet music books her daughter stores in a large wicker basket, and settle on a thick Neil Diamond compilation—even though these are songs we might never have listened to when we were younger. We choose this collection because it contains stirring music and lyrics and they have arranged the tunes for less difficult phrasing. And then I remember a Diamond work Johanna used to tease me with by altering the words from "Girl, you'll be a woman soon" to "*Boy*, you'll *need* a woman soon."

Johanna croons slightly off key when we attempt that song and a few more, however there are instances when she hits several notes in a row—sometimes through an entire tune. I'm rusty for sure, but can often play a number of bars before missing a chord or two—and occasionally squeak through a handful of titles without hitting a clam. "I've Been This Way Before" becomes a favorite of ours.

These performances don't bother Faith and Andrew—or they don't let on if they do. This could be because they—like me—are pleased to see Jo smile, no matter what the reason.

Johanna's finished the landscape painting and—between frequent visits upstairs to that panorama—devotes most of her efforts to a new canvas. This one features the view from a large bay window. Framed by plants and located several stories above ground, it opens to what resembles Tompkins Square Park. A green aura from the Chrysler Building's crown splashes across the top of the piece. In swirling snow, stick-figure-like images scurry to and fro on paths and sidewalks—past nearby trees and lampposts.

At times, Johanna grows disenchanted with where some characters in her painting end up. On those occasions, it's not unusual to wake the next day and discover a couple—last seen leaning against a fence—erased by flurries, and now walking hand in hand down a halo-lamped lane, deep into the park.

About the Author

Peter Sarno taught literature and memoir courses at the University of Massachusetts, Boston and has published essays, reviews, and short stories. While a graduate student at UMass, he won the Donald E Cookson prize in nonfiction. His work has appeared in *The Boston Globe*, *Music World* magazine, *Sweet Potato*, Gannet newspapers, Gatehouse Media, and other outlets. *Visions of Johanna* is his first published novel.

Book Group / Discussion Questions

1. What roles do place/setting/neighborhoods play in the novel? Think of Chelsea, Appleton, Avon, Revere, Boston, the East Village, etc. Is the author able to anchor characters and readers to those locations? How is this accomplished? How do shore and inland locations set mood?

2. How are families depicted? Fathers—present and absent—are portrayed. Matt's mother is very present—why is that? Can you name and discuss some of the parents and the impact they had on the various characters?

3. How and when are food and meals employed?

4. What role does gardening play in the story? Flora and fauna?

5. How are the concepts of faith and hope introduced? How do hope and faith influence how the world is seen?

6. What are the visions of Johanna? Who have them?

7. Most of the relationship between Matt and Johanna takes place during the decade of the '80s. Were you able to recognize this? How or why? What was happening in the '80s that affected the characters?

8. What role—if any—does feminism play in the lives of the characters—both young and old?

9. Who are some of the female artists touched on in this novel? What role might their art play?

10. Are you able to name some of the allusions to specific paintings, films, songs, and literary works of art? What might be their significance?

11. How is the concept of equilibrium/balance addressed?

12. What role does music play in the lives of various characters?

13. What role do Johanna's jobs play in the novel? Why does she turn down the Andover job and accept the New York job? What about Matt's work?

14. In some ways, railroads/rail travel becomes a leitmotif in the story. What might be its significance? What are some other modes of transportation referenced?

15. How does hidden trauma play out in the novel? Why is Matt so reluctant to share his secret? And why doesn't Johanna tell Matt about her past? What roles do guilt and shame play in Matt and Johanna's traumas?

16. What fears are introduced? How do the characters address them? Do they?

17. What are the various mental health issues presented? How do some of the characters deal with them? How is mental illness handled in the novel? What role does our culture—then and now—play in managing mental illness?

18. What efforts did Johanna and other members of her generation make in order to support the women's movement? While reading the novel, did you believe that she and others were successful in having any impact in that regard? How? Why? Based on the June 2022 Supreme Court decision regarding Roe v Wade, what other tactics do you think might be employed to ensure that women receive equal rights?

19. How does Matt become a memory-keeper? Whose memories is he trying to preserve? What do we know now about dementia that we didn't know in the '80s?

20. Were you satisfied with the ending? Why? Why not? What might you have done differently? What were you hoping would happen?

Information / Resources

This list has not been presented as an extensive one.

When several of the events depicted in *Visions of Johanna* occurred, many—if not most—of the associations included below did not exist. PFP Publishing does not endorse and has no affiliation with these firms and recommends that you contact your primary care provider, if possible, for local and more patient-specific resources.

- National Eating Disorders Association (NEDA)
https://www.nationaleatingdisorders.org/
Helpline (800) 931-2237

- John Hopkins Medicine: *Bulimia Nervosa*
https://www.hopkinsmedicine.org/health/conditions-and-diseases/eating-disorders/bulimia-nervosa

- Child Mind Institute: *Helping children cope after a traumatic event*
https://childmind.org/guide/helping-children-cope-after-a-traumatic-event/

- National Suicide Prevention Lifeline
1-800-273-TALK (8255)

- National Alliance on Mental Illness
https://www.nami.org/help

- **Substance Abuse and Mental Health Services Administration (SAMHSA):** *Recognizing and treating child traumatic stress*
https://www.samhsa.gov/child-trauma/recognizing-and-treating-child-traumatic-stress
SAMHSA's National Helpline
1-800-662-HELP (4357)

- **The International Association for Premenstrual Disorders (IAPMD) -** https://iapmd.org/

- **American Pregnancy Association:** *After a Miscarriage: Surviving Emotionally*
https://americanpregnancy.org/getting-pregnant/pregnancy-loss/miscarriage-surviving-emotionally/

- **M.E.N.D. (Mommies Enduring Neonatal Death):** *Miscarriage, Stillbirth & Infant Loss Support*
https://www.mend.org/

- **Mayo Clinic:** *Bipolar Disorder*
https://www.mayoclinic.org/diseases-conditions/bipolar-disorder/symptoms-causes/syc-20355955

- **National Domestic Violence Hotline**
https://www.thehotline.org/
Call 1.800.799.SAFE (7233)

- **Childhelp:** National *Child Abuse Hotline*

https://childhelphotline.org/

- **Organizations for Adult Survivors of Abuse**

https://www.childwelfare.gov/organizations/?CWIG Functionsac-
tion=rols:main.dspList&rolType=Custom&RS_ID=67

- **Grief Share**

https://www.griefshare.org

- **The Trevor Project:** *LGBTQ Support*

https://www.thetrevorproject.org/

- **Alzheimer's & Dementia**

https://www.alz.org/

<u>Other Books by PFP/AJAR Contemporaries</u>

***Waking Slow* – Ioanna Opidee**

"*Waking Slow* shines light on not just the extremes of violence, but the more subtle and insidious indignities and inequalities around us. ...[Ioanna] Opidee has given us a sensitive protagonist who walks the uncomfortable, universal line between alienation and acceptance. The book offers a look at what it takes to put the shards back together after a shattering, showing not that it's easy, or fast, but possible."

—Nina MacLaughlin, ***Boston Globe***

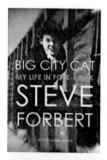

***Big City Cat: My Life in Folk Rock*
- Steve Forbert**

"Like his stunning first album, Steve's compelling first book is very much alive on arrival."

—David Wild
contributing editor, ***Rolling Stone***

***Lunch with Buddha*
- Roland Merullo**

"A beautifully written and compelling story about a man's search for meaning that earnestly and accessibly tackles some well-trodden but universal questions. A quiet meditation on life, death, darkness and spirituality, sprinkled with humor, tenderness and stunning landscapes."

—***Kirkus*** –Starred Review / "Best of 2013"

This Is Paradise: An Irish mother's grief, an African village's plight, and the medical clinic that brought fresh hope to both - Suzanne Strempek Shea

—Named to *Yankee Magazines'* 2014 "New England Wish List."

Smedley's Secret Guide to World Literature - Askold Melnyczuk

"A teen, wired more to his phone than the repercussions of his actions [who] is trying to make sense of his life. Melnyczuk captures these existential dilemmas in a believable voice."

—Clea Simon, *Boston Globe*

Music In and On the Air - Lloyd Schwartz

"Lloyd is my favorite classical music critic. He's a poet, of course, and his gift for language makes him a pleasure to listen to as well as to read."

—Terry Gross, *Fresh Air*

Who Do You Think You Are?: Reflections of a Writer's Life - Joseph Torra

"A memoir about one man's life of writing and self-discovery that flows in a natural way and hums with a sense of honesty." —*Kirkus*